Ecosystems

TEACHER'S GUIDE

SCIENCE AND TECHNOLOGY FOR CHILDREN

NATIONAL SCIENCE RESOURCES CENTER
Smithsonian Institution • National Academy of Sciences
Arts and Industries Building, Room 1201
Washington, DC 20560

NSRC

The National Science Resources Center is operated by the Smithsonian Institution and the National Academy of Sciences to improve the teaching of science in the nation's schools. The NSRC collects and disseminates information about exemplary teaching resources, develops and disseminates curriculum materials, and sponsors outreach activities, specifically in the areas of leadership development and technical assistance, to help school districts develop and sustain hands-on science programs.

STC Project Supporters

National Science Foundation
Smithsonian Institution
U.S. Department of Defense
U.S. Department of Education
John D. and Catherine T. MacArthur Foundation
The Dow Chemical Company Foundation
E. I. du Pont de Nemours & Company
Amoco Foundation, Inc.
Hewlett-Packard Company
Smithsonian Institution Educational Outreach Fund

This project was supported, in part,
by the
National Science Foundation
Opinions expressed are those of the authors
and not necessarily those of the Foundation

ISBN 0-89278-733-3

Published by Carolina Biological Supply Company, 2700 York Road, Burlington, NC 27215.
Call toll free 1-800-334-5551.

This material is based upon work supported by the National Science Foundation under Grant No. ESI-9252947. Any opinions, findings, and conclusions or recommendations expressed in this material are those of the author(s) and do not necessarily reflect the views of the National Science Foundation.

CB787229803

♻ Printed on recycled paper.

Foreword

Since 1988, the National Science Resources Center (NSRC) has been developing Science and Technology for Children (STC), an innovative hands-on science program for children in grades one through six. The 24 units of the STC program, four for each grade level, are designed to provide all students with stimulating experiences in the life, earth, and physical sciences and technology while simultaneously developing their critical-thinking and problem-solving skills.

Sequence of STC Units

Grade	Life, Earth, and Physical Sciences and Technology			
1	Organisms	Weather	Solids and Liquids	Comparing and Measuring
2	The Life Cycle of Butterflies	Soils	Changes	Balancing and Weighing
3	Plant Growth and Development	Rocks and Minerals	Chemical Tests	Sound
4	Animal Studies	Land and Water	Electric Circuits	Motion and Design
5	Microworlds	Ecosystems	Food Chemistry	Floating and Sinking
6	Experiments with Plants	Measuring Time	Magnets and Motors	The Technology of Paper

The STC units provide children with the opportunity to learn age-appropriate concepts and skills and to acquire scientific attitudes and habits of mind. In the primary grades, children begin their study of science by observing, measuring, and identifying properties. Then they move on through a progression of experiences that culminate in grade six with the design of controlled experiments.

Sequence of Development of Scientific Reasoning Skills

Scientific Reasoning Skills	Grades					
	1	2	3	4	5	6
Observing, Measuring, and Identifying Properties	♦	♦	♦	♦	♦	♦
Seeking Evidence Recognizing Patterns and Cycles		♦	♦	♦	♦	♦
Identifying Cause and Effect Extending the Senses				♦	♦	♦
Designing and Conducting Controlled Experiments						♦

The "Focus-Explore-Reflect-Apply" learning cycle incorporated into the STC units is based on research findings about children's learning. These findings indicate that knowledge is actively constructed by each learner and that children learn science best in a hands-on experimental environment where they can make their own discoveries. The steps of the learning cycle are as follows:

- Focus: Explore and clarify the ideas that children already have about the topic.

- Explore: Enable children to engage in hands-on explorations of the objects, organisms, and science phenomena to be investigated.

- Reflect: Encourage children to discuss their observations and to reconcile their ideas.

- Apply: Help children discuss and apply their new ideas in new situations.

The learning cycle in STC units gives students opportunities to develop increased understanding of important scientific concepts and to develop positive attitudes toward science.

The STC units provide teachers with a variety of strategies with which to assess student learning. The STC units also offer teachers opportunities to link the teaching of science with the development of skills in mathematics, language arts, and social studies. In addition, the STC units encourage the use of cooperative learning to help students develop the valuable skill of working together.

In the extensive research and development process used with all STC units, scientists and educators, including experienced elementary school teachers, act as consultants to teacher-developers, who research, trial teach, and write the units. The process begins with the developer researching the unit's content and pedagogy. Then, before writing the unit, the developer trial teaches lessons in public school classrooms in the metropolitan Washington, D.C., area. Once a unit is written, the NSRC evaluates its effectiveness with children by field-testing it nationally in ethnically diverse urban, rural, and suburban public schools. At the field-testing stage, the assessment sections in each unit are also evaluated by the Program Evaluation and Research Group of Lesley College, located in Cambridge, Mass. The final editions of the units reflect the incorporation of teacher and student field-test feedback and of comments on accuracy and soundness from the leading scientists and science educators who serve on the STC Advisory Panel.

The STC project would not have been possible without the generous support of numerous federal agencies, private foundations, and corporations. Supporters include the National Science Foundation, the Smithsonian Institution, the U.S. Department of Defense, the U.S. Department of Education, the John D. and Catherine T. MacArthur Foundation, the Dow Chemical Company Foundation, the Amoco Foundation, Inc., E. I. du Pont de Nemours & Company, the Hewlett-Packard Company, and the Smithsonian Institution Educational Outreach Fund.

Acknowledgments

This unit is adapted from the Bottle Biology Project at the University of Wisconsin, under the direction of Paul Williams, Professor of Plant Pathology. Patricia McGlashan developed and wrote the field-test edition of *Ecosystems*. For this final edition, Carol O'Donnell revised the field-test text and wrote new material. Lynn Miller edited the unit. Martha Vaughan, Lois Sloan, Max-Karl Winkler, Catherine Corder, and Heidi Kupke all contributed to the illustrations in the unit. The unit was trial taught at Troup Middle School in New Haven, CT, in Janice Capone's fifth-grade classroom.

The unit was nationally field-tested in the following school sites with the cooperation of the individuals listed:

The Einstein Project, Green Bay, WI
Coordinator: Cecilia Turriff, Director of Student Programs

Green Bay Area Public School District
Linda Wenzel, Teacher, Christa McAuliffe School
Michael Brown, Teacher, Aldo Leopold School
Gini Mitchell, Teacher, Aldo Leopold School
Ellen VanPay, Teacher, Kennedy School

Denmark Public School District, Denmark, WI
David Ewald, Superintendent
Julie Zipperer, Teacher, Denmark Elementary School

West DePere Public School District, West DePere, WI
Wendee Draves, Teacher, Westwood Elementary School

Green Bay Area Catholic Diocese, Green Bay, WI
Mary Sturm-Johnson, Teacher, St. Joseph School

Redwood City School District, San Mateo County, CA
Coordinator: Rita Orlandini, Science Resource Teacher
Charlene Eng, Teacher, John Gill School
Frank Silva, Teacher, John Gill School

Menlo Park City School District, San Mateo County, CA
Elain McCreight, Teacher, Encinal School

Fulton County School District, Atlanta, GA
Coordinator: Judy Dennison, Elementary Science Coordinator
Kitty Reeves, Teacher, Oak Knoll Elementary School
Carl Golden, Teacher, Love T. Nolan Elementary School
Ann Daly, Teacher, Medlock Bridge Elementary School

Academy School District 20, Colorado Springs, CO
Coordinator: Barbara Betzler, Teacher, Antelope Trails Elementary School
Bonnie Turnbull, Teacher, Pioneer Elementary School
Melanie McEvoy, Teacher, Douglass Elementary School
Leslie Billiard, Teacher, Pioneer Elementary School

Buffalo Public School District, Buffalo, NY
Coordinator: Mary Jean Syrek, Project Team Science
Julie Bukowski, Teacher, Highgate Heights Elementary School
Laura Dierken, Teacher, Highgate Heights Elementary School
Janine Galter-Blue, Teacher, Hamlin Park Elementary School
Shirley Ingram, Teacher, Lincoln Academy
Roberta Lewis, Teacher, Futures Academy
Melinda Long, Teacher, Charles R. Drew Science Magnet

The technical review of *Ecosystems* was conducted by Robert McIntosh, Professor Emeritus, University of Notre Dame, Notre Dame, IN, and by Thomas E. Lovejoy, Assistant Secretary for External Affairs, Smithsonian Institution, Washington, DC.

The NSRC also would like to thank the following individuals who contributed to the development of this unit:

Peter P. Afflerbach, Associate Professor, National Reading Research Center, University of Maryland, College Park, MD
Rodger Bybee, Associate Director, Biological Sciences Curriculum Study, Colorado Springs, CO
Nathan Erwin, Museum Specialist, O. Orkin Insect Zoo, Museum of Natural History, Smithsonian Institution, Washington, DC
Marilyn Fenichel, Writer/Editor, National Science Resources Center, Washington, DC
John Greenler, Project Scientist, Co-Coordinator of the Bottle Biology Project, University of Wisconsin, Madison, WI
Robin Greenler, Co-Coordinator of the Bottle Biology Project, University of Wisconsin, Madison, WI
Richard Kaliszweski, Principal, Troup Middle School, New Haven, CT
Dennis Leaf, Chief of the Evaluation and International Section of the Acid Rain Division, U.S. Environmental Protection Agency, Washington, DC

The library staff of the Yale School of Forestry and Environmental Studies, New Haven, CT

Joan McIntosh, former elementary and secondary teacher of science, South Bend, IN

Randy McGinnis, Assistant Professor, Science Education, University of Maryland, College Park, MD

Robert Mellette, Program Director, Troup Middle School, New Haven, CT

Ed Pembleton, Director of Water Resources Program, National Audubon Society, Washington, D.C.

Sil Pembleton, Director of Environmental Studies, Hard Bargain Farm, Accokeeke, MD

Dane Penland, Chief, Imaging and Technology Services Branch, Office of Printing and Photographic Services, Smithsonian Institution, Washington, DC

Adrienne Schure, Educational Media Specialist, New York, NY

Richard Strauss, Photographer, Office of Printing and Photographic Services, Smithsonian Institution, Washington, DC

Rick Vargas, Photographer, Office of Printing and Photographic Services, Smithsonian Institution, Washington, DC

Janet Leonard-Walker, Teacher, Oak View Elementary School, Montgomery County Public Schools, MD

Paul Williams, Professor of Plant Pathology, University of Wisconsin, Madison, WI

Additional thanks go to the following individuals for assistance in developing materials specifically relating to the Chesapeake Bay:

John Bert, Soil Conservationist, Farm and Home Center, Lancaster, PA

Steve Bunker, Director of Protection, Nature Conservancy, Bethesda, MD

Rod Coggin, Director of Public Affairs, Chesapeake Bay Foundation, Annapolis, MD

Elaine Dickinson, Director of Public Affairs, Boat Owners Association of the United States, Alexandria, VA

Lamont Garber, Agricultural Specialist, Chesapeake Bay Foundation, Harrisburg, PA

Larry Sims, President, Maryland Watermen's Association, Annapolis, MD

STC Advisory Panel

Peter P. Afflerbach, Professor, National Reading Research Center, University of Maryland, College Park, MD

David Babcock, Director, Board of Cooperative Educational Services, Second Supervisory District, Monroe-Orleans Counties, Spencerport, NY

Judi Backman, Math/Science Coordinator, Highline Public Schools, Seattle, WA

Albert V. Baez, President, Vivamos Mejor/USA, Greenbrae, CA

Andrew R. Barron, Professor of Chemistry and Material Science, Department of Chemistry, Rice University, Houston, TX

DeAnna Banks Beane, Project Director, YouthALIVE, Association of Science-Technology Centers, Washington, DC

Audrey Champagne, Professor of Chemistry and Education, and Chair, Educational Theory and Practice, School of Education, State University of New York at Albany, Albany, NY

Sally Crissman, Faculty Member, Lower School, Shady Hill School, Cambridge, MA

Gregory Crosby, National Program Leader, U.S. Department of Agriculture Extension Service/4-H, Washington, DC

JoAnn E. DeMaria, Teacher, Hutchison Elementary School, Herndon, VA

Hubert M. Dyasi, Director, The Workshop Center, City College School of Education (The City University of New York), New York, NY

Timothy H. Goldsmith, Professor of Biology, Yale University, New Haven, CT

Patricia Jacobberger Jellison, Geologist, National Air and Space Museum, Smithsonian Institution, Washington, DC

Patricia Lauber, Author, Weston, CT

John Layman, Director, Science Teaching Center, and Professor, Departments of Education and Physics, University of Maryland, College Park, MD

Sally Love, Museum Specialist, National Museum of Natural History, Smithsonian Institution, Washington, DC

Phyllis R. Marcuccio, Associate Executive Director for Publications, National Science Teachers Association, Arlington, VA

Lynn Margulis, Distinguished University Professor, Department of Botany, University of Massachusetts, Amherst, MA

Margo A. Mastropieri, Co-Director, Mainstreaming Handicapped Students in Science Project, Purdue University, West Lafayette, IN

Richard McQueen, Teacher/Learning Manager, Alpha High School, Gresham, OR

Alan Mehler, Professor, Department of Biochemistry and Molecular Science, College of Medicine, Howard University, Washington, DC

Philip Morrison, Professor of Physics Emeritus, Massachusetts Institute of Technology, Cambridge, MA

Phylis Morrison, Educational Consultant, Cambridge, MA

Fran Nankin, Editor, *SuperScience Red*, Scholastic, New York, NY

Harold Pratt, Senior Program Officer, Development of National Science Education Standards Project, National Academy of Sciences, Washington, DC

Wayne E. Ransom, Program Director, Informal Science Education Program, National Science Foundation, Washington, DC

David Reuther, Editor-in-Chief and Senior Vice President, William Morrow Books, New York, NY

Robert Ridky, Professor, Department of Geology, University of Maryland, College Park, MD

F. James Rutherford, Chief Education Officer and Director, Project 2061, American Association for the Advancement of Science, Washington, DC

David Savage, Assistant Principal, Rolling Terrace Elementary School, Montgomery County Public Schools, Rockville, MD

Thomas E. Scruggs, Co-Director, Mainstreaming Handicapped Students in Science Project, Purdue University, West Lafayette, IN

Larry Small, Science/Health Coordinator, Schaumburg School District 54, Schaumburg, IL

Michelle Smith, Publications Director, Office of Elementary and Secondary Education, Smithsonian Institution, Washington, DC

Susan Sprague, Director of Science and Social Studies, Mesa Public Schools, Mesa, AZ

Arthur Sussman, Director, Far West Regional Consortium for Science and Mathematics, Far West Laboratory, San Francisco, CA

Emma Walton, Program Director, Presidential Awards, National Science Foundation, Washington, DC, and Past President, National Science Supervisors Association

Paul H. Williams, Director, Center for Biology Education, and Professor, Department of Plant Pathology, University of Wisconsin, Madison, WI

STC Development and Production Team

Joyce Lowry Weiskopf, Project Director
Wendy Binder, Research Associate
Edward V. Lee, Research Associate
Christopher Lyon, Research Associate
Carol O'Donnell, Research Associate
Katherine Stiles, Research Associate
Amanda Revere, Office Assistant
Don Cammiso, Research Consultant
Judy White, Research Consultant

Dean Trackman, Publications Director
Lynn Miller, Writer/Editor
Max-Karl Winkler, Illustrator
Heidi M. Kupke, Publications Technology Specialist
David Stein, Editorial Assistant
Laura Akgulian, Writer/Editor Consultant
Linda Harteker, Writer/Editor Consultant
Dorothy Sawicki, Writer/Editor Consultant
Lois Sloan, Illustrator Consultant

NSRC Administration

Douglas Lapp, Executive Director

Charles N. Hardy, Deputy Director for Information Dissemination, Materials Development, and Publications

Sally Goetz Shuler, Deputy Director for Development, External Relations, and Outreach

Diane Mann, Financial Officer

R. Gail Thomas, Administrative Officer

Gail Greenberg, Executive Administrative Assistant

Katherine Darke, Administrative Assistant

Karla Saunders, Administrative Assistant

Kathleen Holmay, Public Information Consultant

STC Evaluation Consultants

George Hein, Director, Program Evaluation and Research Group, Lesley College

Sabra Price, Senior Research Associate, Program Evaluation and Research Group, Lesley College

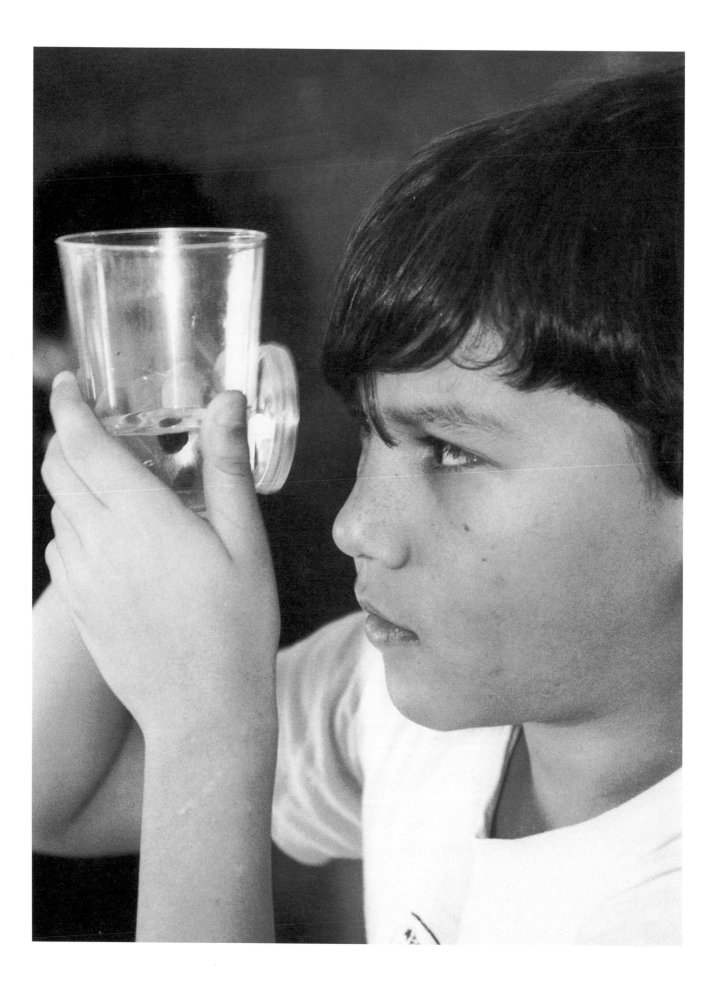

Contents

Foreword iii

Acknowledgments v

Goals for *Ecosystems* 2

Unit Overview and Materials List 3

Important Information on Live Materials 6

Ecosystems Time Line 8

Teaching *Ecosystems* 11

Preparing the Bottles 18

Lesson 1   Thinking about Ecosystems 27

Lesson 2   Setting Up the Terrarium 37

Lesson 3   Setting Up the Aquarium 49

Lesson 4   Adding Animals to the Aquarium 63

Lesson 5   Observing the Completed Aquarium 77

Lesson 6   Adding Animals to the Terrarium 85

Lesson 7   Joining the Terrarium and Aquarium 99

Lesson 8   Upsetting the Stability 107

Lesson 9   Reporting on Pollutants 119

Lesson 10   Planning Pollution Experiments 123

Lesson 11   Setting Up Our Pollution Experiments 135

Lesson 12   Observing Early Effects of Pollution 141

Lesson 13   Where Do the Pollutants Go? 149

Lesson 14   Drawing Conclusions about Our Experiment 157

Lesson 15   Examining a Real Environmental Problem 169

Lesson 16   Holding the Mini-Conference: A Look at Trade-offs 189

Post-Unit Assessment 193

Additional Assessments 197

Bibliography: Resources for Teachers and Students 205

Appendix A   Tips on Receiving and Maintaining Live Materials 213

Appendix B   Reading Selection: Guppies 217

Appendix C   Preparing Two-Piece Bottles with Rigid Bases 221

Goals for *Ecosystems*

In this unit, students explore the web of relationships that link organisms to each other and to their natural environment. From their experiences, they develop an understanding of the following concepts, skills, and attitudes.

Concepts

■ An ecosystem is a community of organisms and its interaction with its environment.

■ Organisms can be categorized by the functions they serve in an ecosystem: producers, consumers, or decomposers.

■ Organisms in an ecosystem have dependent and interdependent relationships, which can be illustrated by food webs.

■ Factors that affect growth and reproduction of organisms in an ecosystem include light, water, temperature, and soil.

■ Natural and human-made events can "disturb" an ecosystem.

■ A pollutant is anything that can harm living organisms when too much of it is released into an ecosystem. Pollution is the condition that results when pollutants interact with the environment.

■ Pollutants can affect the stability of an ecosystem; solutions can be developed to minimize or alleviate the effects of pollutants.

■ Model ecosystems can be used to learn more about the complex relationships that exist on earth.

Skills

■ Using a hand lens, pH paper, measuring devices, and other testing equipment appropriately.

■ Conducting, recording, and organizing daily observations.

■ Planning, implementing, and analyzing experiments and drawing conclusions from the results.

■ Making and testing predictions.

■ Identifying ecosystems as stable or disturbed and recognizing whether the causes of a disturbed ecosystem are natural or human-made.

■ Reading for more information about ecosystems and pollution.

■ Communicating information through writing, drawing, and discussion.

■ Applying previously learned information to analyze a problem and suggest solutions.

Attitudes

■ Developing sensitivity toward living things and understanding that human behavior can positively or negatively affect them.

■ Respecting evidence from an experiment and recognizing that evidence can inform a decision.

■ Developing an interest in investigating ecosystems.

■ Recognizing the importance of repeating experiments to get valid test results.

Unit Overview and Materials List

By fifth grade, most children have become increasingly curious about the complexity of the world around them and about the relationships between the living and nonliving elements in their environment. News stories, community and school projects, and books that promote ecology introduce them to environmental issues. They are fascinated by ways they can help save the environment and the organisms in it.

No organism on earth lives isolated and independent from all others. Every organism—including humans—exists within a community of living and nonliving things, called an ecosystem. *Ecosystems,* a 16-lesson unit designed for fifth-graders, helps students understand the web of relationships that links organisms to one another and to their natural environment. By constructing, observing, discussing, and reading about both land and water ecosystems in this unit, students can develop a growing sensitivity to living things and what they need to survive.

In the unit, students create a model ecosystem by connecting a terrarium and aquarium. This model ecosystem contains both living and nonliving elements. Throughout the unit, students nurture the ecosystems within the ecocolumn, observe changes in each environment, and prepare for pollution experiments to determine the effects of pollutants on organisms in general in an ecosystem.

In the first lesson, students discuss what they already know about "ecosystems" and what they would like to learn. In Lesson 2 each pair of students begins to set up their own terrarium with soil, seeds (grass, mustard, and alfalfa), gravel, sticks, twigs, and rocks. Students make initial observations and begin to practice recordkeeping by noting precisely what they have put into their terraria.

In Lessons 3 and 4 students set up their aquaria, stocking them with algae, duckweed, elodea, snails, and mosquito fish. While continuing to observe and record information on their terrarium plants from Lesson 2, students begin to record their observations about this newly formed model ecosystem: the aquarium. Students then read about their aquatic organisms and begin to grapple with the concept of interdependence.

In Lesson 5, the class continues to observe and discuss the completed aquaria and growing terrarium plants, and to make predictions about what changes might occur. Having observed plant growth firsthand, students now can learn more about germination by reading about how plants grow from seeds. In Lesson 6, the students add live animals to the terrarium to form yet another model ecosystem, one complete with crickets, isopods, and plants. After physically connecting the two bottled ecosystems into an upright "ecocolumn" in Lesson 7, students are ready to speculate about how one ecosystem might influence the other.

By Lesson 8, most ecosystems are showing obvious signs of change; for example, the crickets may have eaten some of the plants or seeds in the terraria, and newborn mosquito fish or snail eggs may have appeared in the aquaria. When such changes disrupt the ecosystem (for example, with more mosquito fish, the food supply dwindles), the stage is set for a class discussion on "stable" and "disturbed" ecosystems. Students discover that disturbing forces are either natural or human-made. They begin to define an environmental pollutant as "anything that can harm living organisms when too much of it is released into the environment." Student groups prepare for upcoming pollution presentations and experiments by reading about three common pollutants or pollutant by-products: acid rain, road salt, and fertilizer.

In Lesson 9, each of the student groups assigned in Lesson 8 reports on one of the three pollutants, and students begin to see how each pollutant can become a disturbing force in some ecosystems. Lesson 10 offers the class experience in systematically planning an experiment and introduces students to the necessity of experimental controls.

Then, in Lessons 11 through 13, student teams use ecocolumns that do not contain animals to conduct several experiments simulating the effects of the three pollutants on the ecosystems. After observing and recording these effects, students analyze their experimental data and draw some initial conclusions about how such pollutants might affect the ecocolumns that contain animals.

In Lesson 14, students report on their team experiments and pool data to arrive at a group consensus. The class begins to perceive that experimental results sometimes vary and are not always clear-cut, and that differing results can provide useful food for thought. As a final activity, students read about a real ecosystem in danger, the Chesapeake Bay.

Switching their focus from the model ecosystems to the vast ecosystem of the Chesapeake Bay, students discover that many of the bay's pollution problems mirror those in the class experiments. Armed with firsthand knowledge gained through the experimental experience, they are ready to break into small groups to analyze the bay situation from several points of view: the waterman, dairy farmer, land developer, recreational boater, and resident of the bay watershed area.

In Lesson 15, students identify their group's contribution to the bay's problems, propose possible solutions, and begin to grapple with the trade-offs involved. These trade-offs become even more evident in Lesson 16, when each group applies role-playing techniques to make a presentation outlining its particular point of view.

Faced with a number of different perspectives, students come to understand that environmental problems are complex. These problems involve many different interest groups and often require the groups to make trade-offs or compromises in order to reach workable solutions. At the same time, students are left with a powerful realization: There are a number of steps every one of us can take to help address the environmental problems in the world around us.

This is an exciting unit for students. They get to work with living creatures, become investigative experimenters, and draw parallels between the dramatic events occurring inside their model ecocolumns and those that occur every day, all over the world. Don't be surprised if some of the questions students ask go beyond what you know or can find out. Because ecological relationships are complex, research findings continue to change, and people have widely differing opinions about environmental issues. No one can provide all the answers. What you as a teacher can do is help students learn how to continue to find out for themselves.

Materials List

Below is a list of materials and organisms needed for the *Ecosystems* unit. Please note that the metric and English equivalent measurements in this unit are approximate.

1	*Ecosystems* Teacher's Guide
15	*Ecosystems* Student Activity Books
1	aquarium thermometer
13	holding tanks
15	medium-sized binder clips
15	fine-point permanent markers
1	knife with a sharp point
1	bag of gravel, 17 kg (35 lb)
15	droppers
15	hand lenses
50	clear plastic cups, 300 ml (10 oz)
15	spoons
15	metric rulers
8	small dipnets
22	square pieces of fiberglass screen, 10 cm (4 in) square
1	bag of soil, 9 kg (20 lb)
60	paper cups, 30 ml (1 oz)
600–650	each of grass, alfalfa, and mustard seeds
1	roll of wide transparent sealing tape, 5 cm (2 in)
8	sets of metric/standard measuring spoons
6	funnels
1	bottle of vinegar, 500 ml (1 pt)
1	container of plant fertilizer, 240 ml (8 oz)
1	container of table salt, 450 g (1 lb)
4	rolls of pH test paper
1	bottle of tap water conditioner (dechlorinating solution)
1	VHS videotape *Living on the Edge,* a Chesapeake Bay Foundation film
*	44 sprigs elodea
*	330 duckweed plants
*	4 jars of algae
*	30 pond snails
*	30 *Gambusia* (mosquito fish)
*	30 crickets
*	30 isopods

**	30 pairs of scissors
**	1 science notebook per student
**	hole punch (for record sheets)
**	70–80 2-liter clear plastic soda bottles with caps
**	22 small rubber bands
**	1 box of toothpicks
**	15 index cards
**	Buckets or dishpans
**	Rags or sponges
**	Paper towels
**	Whisk broom
**	Newsprint
**	Overhead transparencies
**	Markers
**	Newspapers
**	Leaf matter
**	Twigs
**	Stones
**	45 liters (12 gal) of prepared water
**	leaf lettuce
**	2 slices of potato or apple
**	several pieces of dog kibble
**	1 straight pin

*Note: You will need to order these living materials using the two pre-paid order cards enclosed with the kit. Refer to pg. 6 for information on ordering.

Guppies can be used instead of *Gambusia*. If you use guppies, please refer to Appendix B.

**Note: These items are not included in the kit. They are available in most schools or can be brought from home.

Important Information on Live Materials

Ordering Live Materials

If you are using the *Ecosystems* kit of materials from Carolina Biological Supply Company, you will need to order live materials separately by completing the enclosed prepaid order cards.

■ Green card: To order the elodea, duckweed, algae, snails, and mosquito fish for Lessons 3 and 4

■ White card: To order the crickets and isopods for Lesson 6

Before you begin the unit, decide when you need to receive each group of materials (see *Ecosystems* Time Line, pg. 8). These dates will depend on your schedule for teaching the lessons. Carolina Biological Supply Company must receive each card at least 20 business days before your requested delivery date. (If you wish, you can send the cards together before you start the unit.) For this unit, you will receive the live materials in two separate shipments. Each time you send in an order card, remember to do the following:

■ Choose your desired date of arrival. It should be a Wednesday or a Thursday, because your live materials will be shipped on a Monday or a Tuesday.

■ Indicate the requested date of arrival on your order card.

■ Before these dates, prepare for the arrival of the organisms. Collect the needed water and store it in your room to equalize the temperature (see Appendix A, pg. 213).

■ Alert your school's front office to the expected arrival date. Arrange for the boxes to be brought to your room **immediately** upon delivery. Plan to teach the lesson soon afterward.

■ Find out whether exterminators are scheduled to visit your school. If so, be sure they do not treat your classroom while you are teaching the unit.

■ Open the carton and remove the organisms as soon as they arrive (see Appendix A). Label everything.

■ Preview each lesson. Some have specific suggestions for handling the live materials needed that day.

If you are not using the *Ecosystems* kit from Carolina Biological Supply Company, be sure to contact your supplier to establish a delivery schedule.

Management Tips

The plants must be growing when you add the crickets and isopods to the terraria in Lesson 6; otherwise, there will be no food source for the animals and they may die. This growth process takes five to eight days, so plan accordingly. As noted in the *Ecosystems* Time Line on pg. 9, there is a suggested break between Lessons 3 and 4 so that students can observe plant growth in the aquaria and terraria. Keep this break in mind when you choose the arrival date for the second set of live materials for Lesson 6. If you do not take this break, have both sets of live materials delivered at the same time.

If you teach this unit during the colder months of the year, you may need to provide a heat source for the mosquito fish, depending on the temperature variance in your classroom. Mosquito fish will survive in temperatures between 4°C and 38°C (40°F and 100°F) but the optimum temperature for their breeding is 24°C (75°F) plus or minus five degrees.

Why Use these Organisms

The organisms in this unit were thoroughly researched before they were selected. The selection criteria for each organism included the following:

■ The organism supports the goals of the unit.

■ The organism is easy to use in the classroom.

- The organism is available year-round.

- The organism can be cultured or raised (often in a laboratory); therefore, the population of the organism in the wild will not be depleted.

- If the organism is not culturable, research has shown that collecting it from its natural environment will not affect its population or the existing food webs.

- The organism is unlikely to harm local ecosystems.

If you decide to substitute other organisms for those used in this unit, please keep these criteria in mind.

Note: For information on what to do with live materials when the unit is over, see pg. 216 of Appendix A.

Ecosystems Time Line

The *Ecosystems* Time Line on pg. 9 is designed to help you plan your schedule for teaching the unit. With the time line, you can calculate the number of class periods needed for each lesson, anticipate lesson starting dates, and plan for suggested breaks. Remember, the times given for teaching the lessons are approximations and will differ from class to class.

An Important Note about Bottles

Before you begin the unit, the class must collect approximately 70 to 80 2-liter clear plastic soda bottles.

■ 3 bottles for each pair of students to build an ecocolumn

■ 21 bottles to create seven class ecocolumns for the pollution experiments in Lesson 11

■ 8 bottles to hold the pollution solutions in Lesson 11

The ecocolumns fit together best when they are constructed of three sturdy bottles of the same brand.

Before beginning Lesson 1, you will need to prepare the bottles to build the ecocolumns. Use the instructions and suggestions in Preparing the Bottles, pg. 18, to decide what method you will use. Preparation time will depend on which method you choose.

Note: These instructions have been written for one-piece bottles with flanged bases. If you are using two-piece bottles with rigid bases, follow the instructions in Appendix C.

Suggested Breaks Between Lessons

A three-day break is suggested between Lessons 3 and 4 and between Lessons 12 and 13. (The seeds need time to germinate between Lessons 3 and 4, and students will need to observe their polluted ecocolumns between Lessons 12 and 13.) Extending the time between Lessons 12 and 13 will allow the students to observe pronounced effects in their polluted ecocolumns. Plan ahead for the break and prepare additional activities accordingly. The Bibliography can help you plan environmental experiments or select additional classroom reading materials.

When to Assign Reading Selections within Each Lesson

Reading selections for the appropriate lessons are listed on the time line. They can be assigned for homework, during the language arts period, or during your students' free time. Decide how you would like to handle reading selections as you teach each lesson.

Estimated Time Needed to Teach the Unit

On average, the unit's lessons may take approximately 25 classroom sessions to complete (assuming an average class period is 45 minutes long). Additional time may be needed to complete assigned reading selections. Together, the final presentations in Lesson 16, the post-unit assessment, and the additional assessments may take up to a week. If you include the suggested breaks, plan for the unit to take approximately eight to nine weeks.

Ecosystems Time Line

Lesson	Estimated Time Needed	Number of Sessions Needed	Estimated Starting Date
Order live materials for Lessons 3 and 4	At least 10 business days from the date the card reaches CBSC to the arrival date. The arrival date should coincide with Lessons 3 and 4.		Mailing date for green card: Arrival date:
Order live materials for Lesson 6	At least 10 business days from the day the card reaches CBSC to the arrival date. The arrival date should coincide with Lesson 6.		Mailing date for white card: Arrival date:
Preparing the bottles	Time depends on the method you choose (see pg. 20)	Could be done as homework or in class	
1	Set up notebooks: 10 min Lesson: 45 min		
2	Lesson: 50 min		
3	Lesson: 45 min Reading selection		
Break	3–4 days	Observe plants	
4	Lesson: 1½ hr Reading selections	Two	
5	Lesson: 45 min Reading selection		
6	Lesson: 45 min Reading selections **Note:** The terrarium plants should be grown before beginning Lesson 6.		
7	Lesson discussion: 45 min Constructing the ecocolumns and final activities: 45 min	Two	
8	Lesson: 45 min Reading selection Mid-unit self-assessment (see additional assessments, pg. 197): 15 min		

Ecosystems Time Line, *(continued)*

Lesson	Estimated Time Needed	Number of Sessions Needed	Estimated Starting Date
9	Reading selections Presentations and observations: 50 min		
10	Lesson: 40 min Groups complete Record Sheet 10-A: 30 min	Two	
11	Lesson: 45 min Final activities: 30 min	Two	
12	Lesson: 50 min		
Possible break to observe pollution effects	3–4 days	Possible planned activities	
13	Lesson: 50 min Record Sheet 13-A		
14	Lesson: 45 min Reading selection *Living on the Edge* videotape: 15 min		
15	Lesson, point of view sheets, and Record Sheet 15-A: 50 min Final activities: 30 min	Two	
16	Group presentations: Time depends on type of presentations selected Final activities: 30 min		
Post-unit assessment	50 min		
Additional assessments	Time depends on which assessment(s) you choose to complete Assessment 1: 20 min Assessment 2: 45 min		

Teaching *Ecosystems*

The following information on unit structure, teaching strategies, materials, and assessment will help you give students the guidance they need to make the most of their hands-on experiences with this unit.

Unit Structure

How Lessons Are Organized in the Teacher's Guide: Each lesson in the *Ecosystems* Teacher's Guide provides you with a brief overview, lesson objectives, key background information, materials list, advance preparation instructions, step-by-step procedures, final activities, and helpful management tips. Many of the lessons include recommended guidelines for assessment. Lessons also frequently indicate opportunities for curriculum integration. Look for the following icons that highlight extension ideas:

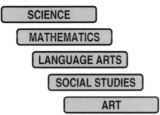

Please note that all record sheets, blackline masters, student instructions, and reading selections may be copied and used in conjunction with the teaching of this unit.

Student Activity Book: The *Ecosystems* Student Activity Book accompanies the Teacher's Guide. Written specifically for students, this activity book contains simple instructions and illustrations to help students understand how to conduct the activities in this unit. The Student Activity Book also will help students follow along with you as you guide each lesson, and it will provide guidance for students who may miss a lesson (or who do not immediately grasp certain activities or concepts). In addition to previewing each lesson in the Teacher's Guide, you may find it helpful to preview the accompanying lesson in the Student Activity Book.

The lessons in the Student Activity Book are divided into the following sections, paralleling the Teacher's Guide:

■ **Think and Wonder** sketches for students a general picture of the ideas and activities of the lesson described in the **Overview and Objectives** of the Teacher's Guide

■ **Materials** lists the materials students and their partners or teammates will be using

■ **Find Out for Yourself** flows in tandem with the steps in the **Procedure** section of the Teacher's Guide and briefly and simply walks students through the lesson's activities

■ **Ideas to Explore,** which frequently echoes the **Extensions** section in the Teacher's Guide, gives students additional activities to try out or ideas to think about

Teaching Strategies

Classroom Discussion: Class discussions, effectively led by the teacher, are important vehicles for science learning. Research shows that the way questions are asked, as well as the time allowed for responses, can contribute to the quality of the discussion.

When you ask questions, think about what you want to achieve in the ensuing discussion. For example, open-ended questions, for which there is no one right answer, will encourage students to give creative and thoughtful answers. You can use other types of questions to encourage students to see specific relationships and contrasts or to help them summarize and draw conclusions. It is good practice to mix these questions. It also is good practice always to give students "wait time" before expecting them to answer; this will encourage broader participation and more thoughtful answers. You will want to monitor responses, looking for additional situations that invite students to formulate hypotheses, make generalizations, and explain how they arrived at a conclusion.

Brainstorming: Brainstorming is a whole-class exercise in which students contribute their thoughts about a particular idea or problem. When used to introduce a new science topic, it can be a stimulating and productive exercise. It also is a useful and efficient way for the teacher to find out what students know and think about a topic. As students learn the rules for brainstorming, they will become increasingly adept in their participation.

To begin a brainstorming session, define for students the topics about which they will share ideas. Explain the following rules to students:

■ Accept all ideas without judgment.

■ Do not criticize or make unnecessary comments about the contributions of others.

■ Try to connect your ideas to the ideas of others.

Webbing: Webbing enables you to record ideas in a graphic display with the main subject at the center, or nucleus, of the web. The advantage of webbing is that it identifies relationships between related ideas and the nucleus. Webbing helps students recognize what they already know about a subject and invites them to make as many associations as they can about it. "Concept mapping" and "clustering" are other names for webbing activities. Students can use webbing during a brainstorming session or to record ideas in their notebooks.

Cooperative Learning Groups: One of the best ways to teach hands-on science is to arrange students in small groups of two or four. *Ecosystems* begins with the students working in pairs. These pairs are later joined in the unit to form cooperative teams. The teams performing the same experimental tasks join to share ideas.

There are several advantages to this organization. It provides a small forum for students to express their ideas and get feedback. It also offers students a chance to learn from each other by sharing ideas, discoveries, and skills. With coaching, students can develop important interpersonal skills that will serve them well in all aspects of life.

As students work, they will often find it productive to talk about what they are doing, resulting in a steady hum of conversation. If you or others in the school are accustomed to a quiet room, this new, busy atmosphere may require some adjustment.

Venn Diagrams: The Venn diagram is a useful tool for sorting, classifying, and comparing information. Within this unit, you and your students will use a Venn diagram to discover ways aquarium and terrarium plants are alike and different. Information that relates to one idea is

Figure T-1

Webbing an idea

written inside one of the circles. Information about a similar yet different idea is written inside another circle. Information common to both ideas is written in the area of intersection.

Learning Centers: You can give supplemental science materials a permanent home in the classroom in a spot designated as the learning center. Students can use the center in a number of ways: as an "on your own" project center, as an observation post, as a trade-book reading nook, or simply as a place to spend unscheduled time when assignments are done. To keep interest in the center high, change the learning center or add to it often. Here are a few suggestions of items to include:

■ Science trade books on aquatic and terrestrial environments, pollution problems, and environmental problems (see the Bibliography for suggested titles).

■ Audiovisual materials on related subjects, such as ponds, forests, insects, fish, and pollution problems (see the Bibliography for video titles).

■ Items contributed by students for sharing, such as magazine or newspaper articles, pictures, insect collections, maps, small plants or animals, and models.

Materials

Safety Notes: This unit does not contain anything of a highly toxic nature, but common sense dictates that nothing be put in the mouth. In fact, it is good practice to tell your students that, in science class, materials are never tasted. Students may also need to be reminded that certain items, such as toothpicks, droppers, knives, straight pins, and scissors should be used only as directed.

Organization of Materials: To help ensure an orderly progression through the unit, you will need to establish a system for storing and distributing materials. Being prepared is the key to success. Here are a few suggestions:

- Read through the Materials List on pg. 5. Begin to collect the items you will need that are not provided in the kit.

- Organize your students so that they are involved in distributing and returning materials. If you have an existing network of cooperative groups, delegate the responsibility to one member of each group.

- Organize a distribution center and instruct your students to pick up and return supplies to that area. A cafeteria-style approach works especially well when there are large numbers of items to distribute.

- Look at each lesson ahead of time. Some have specific suggestions for handling materials needed that day.

- Minimize cleanup by providing each working group with a cleanup box and a packet of paper towels. Students can put disposable materials into this box and clean off their tables at the end of each lesson.

- Refer to pg. 6 and Appendix A: Tips on Receiving and Maintaining Live Materials for more specific information on living materials.

- Management tips are provided in the unit. Look for the icon at the right:

Assessment

Philosophy: In the Science and Technology for Children program, assessment is an ongoing, integral part of instruction. Because assessment emerges naturally from the activities in the lessons, students are assessed in the same manner in which they are taught. They may, for example, perform experiments, record their observations, or make oral presentations. Such assessments permit the examination of processes as well as of products, emphasizing what students know and can do.

The learning goals in STC units include a number of different science concepts, skills, and attitudes. Therefore, a number of different strategies are provided to help you assess and document your students' progress toward the goals (see Figure T-2). These strategies also will help you report to parents and appraise your own teaching. In addition, the assessments will enable your students to view their own progress, reflect on their learning, and formulate further questions for investigation and research.

Figure T-2 summarizes the goals and assessment strategies for this unit. The left-hand column lists the individual goals for the *Ecosystems* unit and the lessons in which they are addressed. The right-hand column identifies lessons containing assessment sections to which you can turn for specific assessment strategies. These strategies are summarized as bulleted items.

Assessment Strategies: The assessment strategies in STC units fall into three categories: matched pre- and post-unit assessments, embedded assessments, and additional assessments.

The first lesson of each STC unit is a *pre-unit assessment* designed to give you information about what the whole class and individual students already know about the unit's topic and what they want to find out. It often includes a brainstorming session during which students share their thoughts about the topic through exploring one or two basic questions. In the *post-unit assessment* following the final lesson, the class revisits the pre-unit assessment questions, giving you two sets of comparable data that indicate students' growth in knowledge and skills.

Throughout a unit, assessments are incorporated, or embedded, into lessons. These *embedded assessments* are activities that occur naturally within the context of both the individual lesson and the unit as a whole; they are often indistinguishable from instructional activities. By providing structured activities and guidelines for assessing students' progress and thinking, embedded assessments contribute to an ongoing, detailed profile of growth. In many STC units, the last lesson is an embedded assessment that challenges students to synthesize and apply concepts or skills from the unit.

continued on pg. 16

Ecosystems: Goals and Assessment Strategies

Concepts	
Goals	**Assessment Strategies**
An ecosystem is a community of organisms and its interaction with its environment. Lessons 1–16	Lessons 1, 7, 11–12, 16 ■ Pre- and post-unit assessments ■ Class discussions and brainstorming sessions ■ Students' observations ■ Notebook entries ■ Class presentations ■ Record sheets
Organisms can be categorized by the functions they serve in an ecosystem: producers, consumers, or decomposers. Lessons 1–12	Lessons 1, 6, 12 ■ Pre-unit and post-unit assessments ■ Notebook entries ■ Record sheets ■ Class discussions
Organisms in an ecosystem have dependent and interdependent relationships, which can be illustrated by food webs. Lessons 1–12	Lessons 1, 7, 11–12 ■ Pre- and post-unit assessments ■ Venn diagrams ■ Webbing activity ■ Class discussions ■ Teacher's observations
Factors that affect growth and reproduction of organisms in an ecosystem include light, water, temperature, and soil. Lessons 1–14	Lessons 1, 7–11 ■ Pre-unit and post-unit assessments ■ Notebook entries ■ Class discussions ■ Webbing activities ■ Oral presentations ■ Record sheets
Natural and human-made events can "disturb" an ecosystem. Lessons 1, 7–9, 11, 13–15	Lessons 1, 7, 9, 11–12 ■ Pre- and post-unit assessments ■ Notebook entries ■ Class discussions ■ Record sheets
A pollutant is anything that can harm living organisms when too much of it is released into an ecosystem. Pollution is the condition that results when pollutants interact with the environment. Lessons 8–16	Lessons 9, 12 ■ Class discussions ■ Class presentations ■ Class lists
Pollutants can affect the stability of an ecosystem; solutions can help minimize or alleviate the effects of pollutants. Lessons 10–16	Lesson 16 ■ Class presentations ■ Teacher's observations
Model ecosystems can be used to learn more about the complex relationships that exist on earth. Lessons 2–16	Lessons 2, 6–7, 11–12 ■ Lab procedures ■ Teacher observations ■ Class discussions ■ Notebook entries

Skills	
Goals	**Assessment Strategies**
Using a hand lens, pH paper, measuring devices, and other testing equipment appropriately. Lessons 2–12	Lessons 2, 6–7, 10–12 ■ Lab procedures ■ Teacher's observations ■ Record sheets

Skills *(continued)*

Goals	Assessment Strategies
Conducting, recording, and organizing daily observations. Lessons 2–13	Lessons 2, 6–7, 10–12 ▪ Teacher's observations ▪ Record sheets ▪ Students' observations ▪ Lab procedures ▪ Notebook entries
Planning, implementing, and analyzing experiments and drawing conclusions from the results. Lessons 10–16	Lessons 10–12, 16 ▪ Planning and record sheets ▪ Notebook entries ▪ Lab procedures ▪ Teacher's observations
Making and testing predictions. Lessons 1–13	Lessons 1–2, 6–7, 10–12 ▪ Pre- and post-unit assessments ▪ Class discussions ▪ Record sheets ▪ Notebook entries
Identifying ecosystems as stable or disturbed and recognizing the causes of a disturbed ecosystem as natural or human-made. Lessons 1, 7–9	Lessons 1, 7 ▪ Pre- and post-unit assessments ▪ Classroom discussions ▪ Notebook entries
Reading for more information about ecosystems and pollution. Lessons 3–6, 8, 10, 14–16	Lessons 9, 16 ▪ Notebook entries ▪ Class lists ▪ Class presentations
Communicating information through writing, drawing, and discussion. Lessons 1–16	Lessons 1–2, 6–7, 9–12, 16 ▪ Pre- and post-unit assessments ▪ Notebook entries ▪ Class discussions ▪ Class presentations ▪ Record sheets
Applying previously learned information to analyze a problem and suggest solutions. Lessons 10–16	Lesson 16 ▪ Class discussions ▪ Class presentations ▪ Teacher's observations ▪ Record sheets

Attitudes	
Goals	**Assessment Strategies**
Developing sensitivity toward living things and understanding that human behavior can positively or negatively affect them. Lessons 2–16	Lessons 1–2, 6, 9, 11–12, 16 ▪ Pre- and post-unit assessments ▪ Record sheets ▪ Notebook entries ▪ Teacher's observations
Respecting evidence from an experiment and recognizing that evidence can inform a decision. Lessons 10–16	Lessons 10–12, 16 ▪ Record sheets ▪ Teacher's observations ▪ Lab procedures ▪ Class discussions ▪ Class presentations
Developing an interest in investigating ecosystems. Lessons 1–16	Lessons 1–2, 6–7, 9–12, 16 ▪ Pre- and post-unit assessments ▪ Class discussions ▪ Teacher's observations ▪ Notebook entries ▪ Lab procedures
Recognizing the importance of repeating experiments to get valid test results. Lessons 10–13	Lessons 10–12 ▪ Lab procedures ▪ Record sheets ▪ Teacher's observations

continued from pg. 13

Additional assessments can be used to determine students' understanding after the unit has been completed. In these assessments, students may work with materials to solve problems, conduct experiments, or interpret and organize data. In grades three through six, they may also complete self-assessments or paper-and-pencil tests. When you are selecting additional assessments, consider using more than one assessment to give students with different learning styles opportunities to express their knowledge and skills.

Documenting Student Performance: In STC units, assessment is based on your recorded observations, students' work products, and oral communication. All these documentation methods combine to give you a comprehensive picture of each student's growth.

Teachers' *observations and anecdotal notes* often provide the most useful information about students' understanding, especially in the early grades when some students are not yet writing their ideas fluently. Because it is important to document observations used for assessment, teachers frequently keep note cards, journals, or checklists. Many lessons include guidelines to help you focus your observations. The blackline master on pg. 17 provides a format you may want to use or adapt for recording observations. It includes this unit's goals for science concepts and skills.

Work products, which include both what students write and what they make, indicate students' progress toward the goals of the unit. Children produce a variety of written materials during a unit. Record sheets, which include written observations, drawings, graphs, tables, and charts, are an important part of all STC units. They provide evidence of each student's ability to collect, record, and process information. Students' science journals are another type of work product. In grades one and two, journal writings are primarily suggested as extension activities in many lessons. Often a rich source of information for assessment, these journal writings reveal students' thoughts, ideas, and questions over time.

Students' written work products should be kept together in folders to document learning over the course of the unit. When students refer back to their work from previous lessons, they can reflect on their learning. In some cases, students do not write or draw well enough for their products to be used for assessment purposes, but their experiences do contribute to the development of scientific literacy.

Oral communication—what students say formally and informally in class and in individual sessions with you—is a particularly useful way to learn what students know. This unit provides your students with many opportunities to share and discuss their own ideas, observations, and opinions. Some young children may be experiencing such activities for the first time. Encourage students to participate in discussions, and stress that there are no right or wrong responses. Creating an environment in which students feel secure expressing their own ideas can stimulate rich and diverse discussions.

Individual and group presentations can give you insights about the meanings your students have assigned to procedures and concepts and about their confidence in their learning. In fact, a student's verbal description of a chart, experiment, or graph is frequently more useful for assessment than the product or results. Questions posed by other students following presentations provide yet another opportunity for you to gather information. Ongoing records of discussions and presentations should be a part of your documentation of students' learning.

Ecosystems: Observations of Student Performance

STUDENT'S NAME:

Concepts	**Observations**
• An ecosystem is a community of organisms and its interaction with its environment.	
• Organisms can be categorized by the functions they serve in an ecosystem: producers, consumers, or decomposers.	
• Organisms in an ecosystem have dependent and interdependent relationships, which can be illustrated by food webs.	
• Factors that affect growth and reproduction of organisms in an ecosystem include light, water, temperature, and soil.	
• Natural and human-made events can "disturb" an ecosystem.	
• A pollutant is anything that can harm living organisms when too much of it is released into an ecosystem. Pollution is the condition that results when pollutants interact with the environment.	
• Pollutants can affect the stability of an ecosystem; solutions can help minimize or alleviate the effects of pollutants.	
• Model ecosystems can be used to learn more about the complex relationships that exist on earth.	

Skills	
• Using a hand lens, pH paper, measuring devices, and other testing equipment appropriately.	
• Conducting, recording, and organizing daily observations.	
• Planning, implementing, and analyzing experiments and drawing conclusions from the results.	
• Making and testing predictions.	
• Identifying ecosystems as stable or disturbed and recognizing the causes of a disturbed ecosystem as natural or human-made.	
• Reading for more information about ecosystems and pollution.	
• Communicating information through writing, drawing, and discussion.	
• Applying previously learned information to analyze a problem and suggest solutions.	

Preparing the Bottles

This section will help you plan for preparing the bottles needed for the ecocolumns in this unit. A blackline master of student instructions for preparing the bottles is on pgs. 20–21. Read over these instructions, collect the materials, and review the instructions with your students (or student and parent volunteers) before preparing the bottles. Also decide on a place to store the bottle parts.

There are five key steps to preparing the bottles for building an ecocolumn:

- Collecting three bottles for each ecocolumn

- Cleaning the bottles out

- Removing their labels

- Finding boxes for marking the bottles

- Marking and cutting the bottles

Of these five steps, the first four can be done at home. The other step can be done in school before beginning the unit. You may want to solicit the help of parent volunteers to complete this task.

Note: This section has been written for one-piece bottles with flanged bases. If you are using two-piece bottles with rigid bases, follow the bottle preparation instructions in Appendix C.

Collecting the Bottles

Have each pair of students try to bring in three bottles of the same brand for their ecocolumn—the bottles will fit together much more easily. If students are unable to find similar bottles, they can simply exchange bottles or make adjustments.

Very important: Assign several of your students to collect 21 bottles for the seven class ecocolumns. Volunteers will need to remove the bottles' labels, clean the bottles, mark and cut them, and assemble them into seven class ecocolumns. Then in each lesson, these students, or others that you select, will be responsible for adding and maintaining the plants in the ecocolumns. The class ecocolumns will be used in Lessons 11 through 15.

Cleaning the Bottles

Students must rinse the bottles with clean water. Remind your students not to use soap or detergent, because they may harm the living creatures they will put in the ecocolumns later in the unit.

Removing the Labels

Have students remove the labels at home. If the labels do not peel off the bottle, the students will need to heat the glue that holds the labels in place. They can use two methods: "The Hot Water Way" or "The Hair Dryer Way." Both will work well at home, but make certain the students do not use water or air that is too hot (the water should not be over 48°C, or 120°F). If they do, the plastic bottles may become too soft and change shape permanently. Have the students follow the instructions for preparing the bottles.

Finding Marking Boxes

Locate several boxes to use in marking the bottles. Choose boxes as close to the size of the bottles as possible. A large shoe box or the lid to a box of photocopy paper should work.

Marking and Cutting the Bottles

Set up the materials for easy distribution to the students. If possible, arrange to have a parent volunteer help you mark and cut the bottles.

Not all bottles are the same shape or size. On the student instructions, the measurements for marking the bottles are approximate. You may need to help your students adjust the binder clips on the marking boxes so that the lines on their bottles match the lines in the pictures.

While students are marking the bottles, it is a good idea for you or the adult helper to circulate around the room to puncture the marked bottles with a knife. Before you make the puncture, be sure the cap is on or the bottle may collapse. Also use this time to puncture a few holes in the cut-off base of bottle T, which the students will use as the terrarium lid. Students can discard and recycle the other cut-off bottle parts.

After marking and cutting the bottles, students will need to test the fit by actually forming the bottles into an ecocolumn. After they have adjusted or exchanged bottles to fit, have the students clean up and put the bottle pieces away. Let them decide how they will distinguish one team's set of bottles from another (for example, names or team code numbers).

Student Instructions for Preparing the Bottles

In this unit you will connect three 2-liter, clear plastic soda bottles to build an ecocolumn. One bottle will be an aquarium, one a terrarium, and one a connecting piece. To prepare the bottles for your ecocolumn, you will need to do a few things at home.

Collecting the Bottles

■ Bring in three 2-liter, clear plastic soda bottles. **Bring in the bottle caps, too!**

■ Use bottles that have never been creased. Creases are weak spots.

■ Try to find bottles of the same brand. They will fit together much more easily.

Cleaning the Bottles

Rinse the bottles with clean water. **Do not use soap,** because it may harm the living creatures you will put in the ecocolumns later on in the unit.

Removing the Labels

The labels are held on by glue. If you cannot easily peel the labels off, you can remove them in two other ways: "The Hot Water Way" and "The Hair Dryer Way." Heat will easily melt the glue.

The Hot Water Way

1. Put very hot water (but not over 48°C, or 120°F) in the bottle until it is about a quarter full. It is important not to use water that is too hot. If you do, the plastic bottle may become too soft and change shape permanently. Use a thermometer if necessary to check the temperature of the water. Put the cap back on; otherwise, the bottle may collapse when you hold it tightly.

2. Find the place on the bottle where the label is glued. Lay the bottle on its side so the water inside warms the area where the label is glued to the bottle.

3. Wait a few minutes for the glue to soften. Then, with your fingernail, lift a corner of the label and gently peel it off the bottle. If the label doesn't peel easily, wait a little longer or try hotter water.

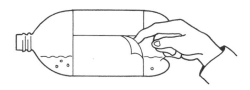

4. Remove the cap and pour out the water. Try this: swirl the bottle around as it starts to empty. The water will form a funnel shape, like a mini-tornado. This way the water empties slowly, and the bottle's sides will not collapse.

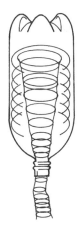

The Hair Dryer Way

1. Find the place on the bottle where the label is glued.

2. Focus the nozzle of the hair dryer on the strip of glue for about 5 to 10 seconds. It's important to use low heat and to keep the hair dryer moving during this time so the plastic does not get too hot and change shape.

Student Instructions for Labeling, Marking, and Cutting the Bottles

Materials   *For every two students*

3 rinsed 2-liter soda bottles with the labels removed
3 bottle caps
1 pair of scissors
1 marking box
1 permanent marking pen
1 medium black binder clip
1 metric ruler

For the class
Marking boxes

For the teacher or adult helper
1 knife

Labeling Each Bottle

Your **ecocolumn** will be made up of three different bottles: the **aquarium, terrarium,** and **connector.**

1. Use your marking pen to mark one bottle **"A"** for **aquarium.**

2. Turn another bottle upside down and mark it **"T"** for **terrarium.**

3. Turn the last bottle upside down and mark it **"C"** for **connector.**

Labeling the Marking Box

Now you must put letters on the marking box so you know where to mark each bottle.

1. Use your marking pen to write the word **"Top"** at one end of the box.

2. Measure 23.5 cm from the top end. Mark this point **"C/T."** (These letters stand for Connector and Terrarium.)

3. Measure 11 cm from the top end. Mark this point **"A"** (for Aquarium).

4. Measure 9.5 cm from the top end. Mark this point **"C"** (for another cut on the Connector).

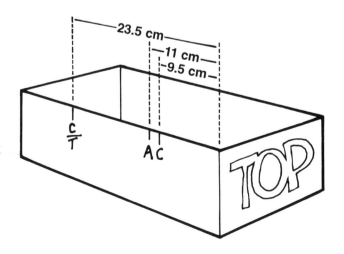

Marking the Bottles

Now you must mark the bottles with lines so you will know where to cut each bottle. Work with your partner. Take turns holding the bottle in the marking box and drawing the lines.

Note: Not all bottles are the same shape or size. When you finish marking, make sure your bottles look like the ones in the pictures. You may need to change some of your marks before you cut the bottles.

1. Make certain that the cap is off bottle **T**. Place bottle **T** in the marking box.

2. Place the **center** of the black binder clip down over the space marked **C/T.** The binder clip will hold your pen in place as you mark the bottles.

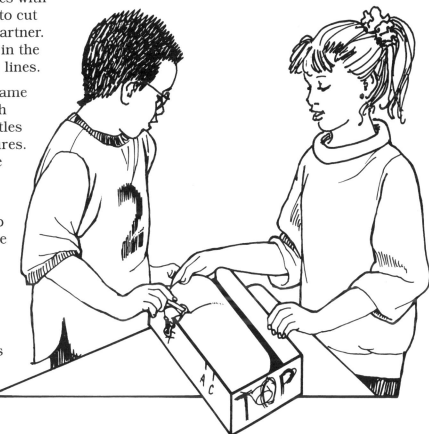

3. Push down the outside loop of the binder clip. Place the marking pen through the inside loop, which should still be up. The pen should be slightly touching the bottle.

4. Have your partner hold the bottle in place and spin it slowly while you hold the pen. Spin the bottle until a line is drawn all the way around it.

5. Take the bottle out of the box and **put the cap back on** it. Look at your bottle. Does your line match the one in the picture? If not, adjust your binder clip and redraw the line.

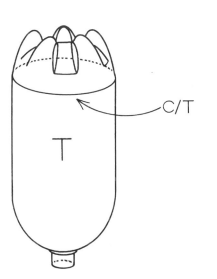

6. While you are working on the next steps, your teacher or an adult helper will come around with a knife to make the first cut on the line for you. This will make it easier for you to get your scissors started when you cut the bottle.

7. Now place bottle **A** in the marking box. Make certain the cap is off the bottle.

8. This time, you will put the center of the binder clip over the letter **A.** Repeat Steps 3 to 5. Mark the bottle all the way around with your pen and replace the cap.

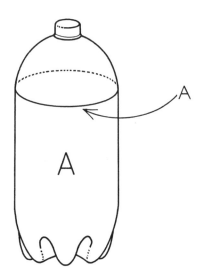

9. Look at your bottle. Is the line in the right place? When your line matches the one in the picture, let your teacher or the adult helper make the first cut on your bottle with a knife.

10. Place bottle **C** in the marking box. First, put the center of the binder clip over the letter **C.** Repeat steps 3 to 5.

11. Now remove the binder clip from the marking box and place the **center** of the binder clip over the letters **C/T.** Mark the bottle all the way around on this spot, too.

12. Remove bottle **C** and put the cap back. Check to make certain the lines are in the right place.

13. When your lines match the ones in the picture, have your teacher or an adult helper make the first cut on both lines.

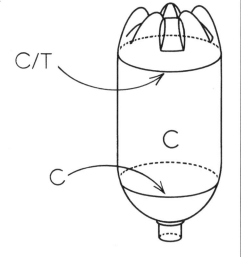

Cutting and Assembling the Bottles

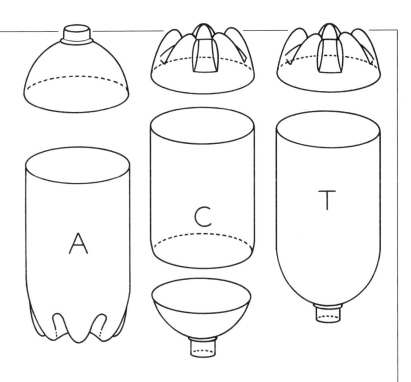

1. For each of your three bottles, place your scissors in the first cut that your teacher made with the knife. Follow the line to cut completely around the bottle.

2. Save the base that you cut from bottle **T.** You will use it for the terrarium lid. Your teacher or an adult will help you cut holes in the lid.

3. Assemble the bottles as shown in the illustration to the right. If the bottles don't fit well together or one bottle slides down into another, try to figure out how to adjust them so that they will fit. You may want to exchange a bottle with another team until the bottles form a good ecocolumn.

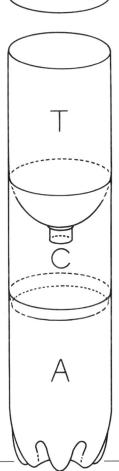

Thinking about Ecosystems

Overview and Objectives

Lesson 1 focuses students on the topic of ecosystems and serves as a pre-unit assessment of their knowledge and questions related to ecosystems. When students share what they know and the questions they have about ecosystems, they begin to consider the relationships that exist between living and nonliving things. A discussion prompted by an illustration of a riverbank provides additional information about ideas regarding these relationships. You can use this information as a baseline when, at the end of the unit, you assess students' growth in concepts and skills.

- Students set up their science notebooks, which they will use to record ideas and observations throughout the unit.

- Students record and discuss their thoughts about how living things depend on each other.

- Students discuss what they would like to find out about how living things depend on each other.

- Students observe and discuss a riverbank environment.

Background

No organism on earth lives isolated and independent from all others. All living things, including microorganisms, exist in a community of living organisms called an **ecosystem.** An ecosystem includes nonliving elements too, such as soil, water, air, and sunlight. A stable ecosystem is virtually self-sustaining in the absence of human interference.

Students may be unfamiliar with the word "ecosystem." It is important for them to focus on the relationships they can see and to develop the idea of interdependence before you introduce this term. As this unit develops, students will create their own definition for the word "ecosystem" on the basis of their experiences with the terraria and aquaria.

"Eco" comes from the Greek word for house, habitat, or environment. So, **ecology** is the science concerned with the relationship of living things to each other and to their natural environment. These complex relationships commonly involve food, protection, shelter, and reproduction. The relationships will become evident in the two ecosystems your students will create.

Throughout this unit, all living things within an ecosystem are referred to as organisms. Scientists usually classify organisms into five kingdoms. The first two kingdoms, Animalia and Plantae (both containing multicellular organisms) are the ones with which your students probably have had the most experience. The animals in this unit are *Gambusia* (or mosquito fish), snails, crickets, and isopods. The plants are elodea, duckweed, ryegrass, mustard, and alfalfa.

Advancements in biology have enabled microbiologists to refine the way they classify the single-celled organisms. The green algae used in this unit are considered members of the kingdom Protoctista, which contains primarily unicellular organisms having a true nucleus. The other kingdom of unicellular organisms, the Prokaryotae, are characterized by the lack of a true cell nucleus.

The two kingdoms Fungi and Prokaryotae are not specifically addressed in this unit. However, mold or other fungi might grow in the ecocolumns, and prokaryotes will certainly be in there. Prokaryotes (bacteria) are crucial to a healthy ecosystem; they participate in the production and removal of the major gases in the atmosphere, and they break down (or decompose) waste, and dead organisms. Without bacteria, other organisms could not survive.

The currently accepted five-kingdom system of classification still leaves many questions about the classification of some organisms unanswered. Continued research on organisms is likely to advance our knowledge and change this system still further. Therefore, although students should know that there are organisms that do not fall into either the plant or animal kingdom, the remaining kingdom names and determining criteria should not be emphasized.

Today's brainstorming session about the riverbank environment (illustrated on pg. 35 in this guide and on pg. 4 in the Student Activity Book) will spark students' thinking about these relationships and will also give you some idea of what they already know. Naturally enough, students will exhibit a wide range of experience, information, and understanding concerning ecosystems. Do not be surprised, however, if students' lists are rather simple and short at this time. At the end of the unit, when the class repeats this activity, you can expect to see some real growth in ideas.

Many students may be able to discuss one of the more obvious relationships in most environments; that is, Who eats what? For example, most students will be able to trace a food chain from the water plants to the fish to the heron; or, somewhat more simply, from the water plants to the duck. But few will know that water plants, like all green plants, use energy from the sun to make their own food (see Figure 1-1).

Figure 1-1

sun ➡ water ➡ plants ➡ fish ➡ raccoon

Energy flow in a riverbank environment

Relationships that students may not recognize are those involving microorganisms, which include decomposers. Decomposers include fungi and bacteria. The ecosystem's "cleanup crew," they dispose of waste matter. Decomposers also unlock valuable nutrients stored in dead organic matter and return them to the soil.

If your students do not raise it, be sure to touch on the need for shelter. This will bring some nonliving elements into the picture. Some creatures will find shelter in cracks along a bank, in bushes, and in dead vegetation. Others will dive into the water, dig burrows in the soil, or hide in decomposing trees.

Materials

For each student
1   science notebook

For every two students
1   *Ecosystems* Student Activity Book

For the class
   Large sheets of newsprint (2 or more) and markers, or overhead
      transparencies (2 or more) and markers
1   overhead transparency of **The Riverbank Environment** (blackline master
      on pg. 35)
1   overhead projector

Preparation

1.   Review this lesson as it is presented in the Student Activity Book.

2.   Obtain the materials needed to record student ideas and questions. Label
      one sheet "How Living Things Depend on Each Other: What We Know Now."
      Label the other "How Living Things Depend on Each Other: What We Would
      Like to Find Out." Hang the two sheets if you are using newsprint.

3.   Make an overhead transparency of **The Riverbank Environment** on pg. 35.

4.   Set up the overhead projector.

5.   Decide how you and your students will set up their science notebooks. You
      may find that a three-ring binder works well, since it gives students a place
      in which to record observations and hold record sheets.

6.   If you have not yet done so, review the section Preparing the Bottles, on pg. 18,
      to decide how to handle the task of removing the labels from the bottles,
      marking the bottles, and cutting them. It is best to prepare these bottles prior
      to Lesson 1 so that Lessons 1 and 2 flow naturally, without a break. However,
      if you have not yet done so, make certain to remove the labels and cut the
      bottles before you begin Lesson 2.

7.   Assign each student a partner to work with for the entire unit.

Management Tip: When you form partners and cooperative groups, consider
mixing children with different levels of reading, writing, and verbal ability. That
way each team has strengths in each area, and students are likely to complement
and work well with each other.

8.   Designate a storage area for the bottle parts.

Procedure

1.   To introduce the goals of the unit, help students understand that they will
      study two different types of environments—an aquarium and a terrarium—
      and learn about the relationships between living things within these
      environments.

2.   Ask students to write today's date in their science notebooks. Let them
      know that they will also put their record sheets in this notebook.

3.   Next, display the two sheets entitled "How Living Things Depend on Each
      Other: What We Know Now," and "How Living Things Depend on Each
      Other: What We Would Like to Find Out." Ask students to record their ideas
      independently in their notebooks.

4. Ask students to share their written responses. Record their ideas and questions as objectively as possible. For an example, see Figure 1-2. Remember, the lists may be short and simple now, but they are likely to be longer and more complex in the post-unit assessment.

    Note: Keep both sheets to use as you proceed through the unit. You will use them again for the post-unit assessment.

Figure 1-2

Sample class lists

HOW LIVING THINGS DEPEND ON EACH OTHER: WHAT WE KNOW NOW

ANIMALS AND HUMANS NEED FOOD, SHELTER AND AIR

ANIMALS NEED HELP OR PROTECTION

ANIMALS MATE TO PRODUCE MORE

WE DEPEND ON SOME ANIMALS FOR MEAT

FOOD CHAIN

FLOWERS NEED SUNLIGHT

ANIMALS NEED TREES FOR OXYGEN

ANIMALS HELP EACH OTHER BUILD HOM

ANIMALS NEED EACH OTHER

HUMANS NEED FOOD

ANIMALS NEED PLANTS

ANIMALS NEED WATER

HOW LIVING THINGS DEPEND ON EACH OTHER: WHAT WE WOULD LIKE TO FIND OUT

ANYTHING WE DON'T KNOW

IF THERE IS A DISEASE IN A FOOD CHAIN, WHAT HAPPENS?

HOW DO BABY FISH SURVIVE UNTIL THEY ARE BIG?

HOW MANY LIVING THINGS ARE IN THE WORLD?

HOW DO YOU TAME AN ANIMAL?

DO ANIMALS POLLUTE?

HOW MANY ANIMALS ARE EXTINCT?

WHAT WOULD HAPPEN IF ALL THE PLANTS DIED?

IF THE FOOD CHAIN IS BROKEN CAN IT BE FIXED?

CAN ANY ANIMAL LIVE WITHOUT OTHER PLANTS AND ANIMALS?

CAN ANY ANIMALS ADAPT TO A POLLUTED ENVIRONMENT?

5. Distribute the Student Activity Books.

6. Show students the illustration of the riverbank environment and have them find this illustration in their Student Activity Books. (Figure 1-3 provides you with a key to the illustration of the riverbank environment.)

Figure 1-3

*Key to the
illustration of
the riverbank
environment*

1. **Heron**
2. **Bee**
3. **Deer**
4. **Dragonfly**
5. **Willow trees**
6. **Beaver**
7. **Lily pad**
8. **Duck**
9. **Diving beetle**
10. **Limpets**
11. **Mare's tail**
12. **Snail**
13. **Freshwater shrimp**
14. **Trout**
15. **Tadpole**
16. **Arrowhead**
17. **Frog**
18. **Swan**
19. **Cattails**

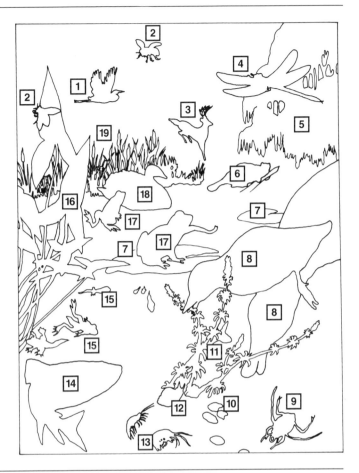

7. Ask students to describe the different kinds of relationships they see. The following questions may help focus the discussion:

   ■ Identify the living things in this environment. How do the plants depend on the animals? How do the animals depend on the plants? How do the animals depend on each other?

   ■ Which of these living things need others in order to survive?

   ■ Identify the nonliving things in this environment. What part do they play in the lives of the living things?

   ■ What might be going on that you cannot see?

8. Then ask students to record in their notebooks some thoughts on the following:

   ■ Describe a situation in nature in which one living thing depends on another living thing.

   ■ Look at the riverbank environment again. Imagine that a group of people begins to set up a city in this area. What will change? List all the changes you can think of.

   ■ What problems might occur when humans interfere with an environment? What could you do to help improve the environment or clear up the problems caused by the humans?

Final Activities

1. If possible, take the class on a field trip to look at the schoolyard environment. Use the following questions to help guide a class discussion:

   ■ What plants live in the schoolyard environment?

   ■ Is there evidence of any animal inhabitants? (Don't forget that people are animals.)

   ■ Are there other living things? (Students may observe fungi.)

   ■ How do the animals depend on the plants for their needs? How do the plants depend on the animals?

   ■ What nonliving things do the plants and animals depend on?

   ■ How did the living things you observed get food, shelter, water, and protection?

2. During the field trip, ask students to collect some materials such as dirt, rocks, and leaf matter for the terraria they will begin building in the next lesson.

3. If you cannot take this field trip, ask students to explore the environment around their homes and collect materials to bring in.

Extensions

LANGUAGE ARTS

1. Ask students to choose one relationship they see in the riverbank environment and write a story about how each of the living things depends on the other.

LANGUAGE ARTS

2. Encourage your students to do library research about plants and animals that live in our forests, lakes, and marshes.

SOCIAL STUDIES

3. Plan a field trip to a local environment: an aquarium, a pond, an arboretum, or even the local pet shop. As an alternative, you might invite a naturalist, zookeeper, fish hobbyist, or pet shop proprietor to visit your class.

Figure 1-4

Visit an aquarium

Assessment

In the section Teaching *Ecosystems,* on pgs. 11 to 17, you will find a detailed discussion about the assessment of students' learning. The specific goals and related assessments for this unit are summarized in Figure T-2, on pgs. 14–15.

In this lesson, students' notebook entries and the ideas they suggest during the class brainstorming session provide important information about their baseline knowledge of ecosystems. This information serves as the first part of the matched pre- and post-unit assessments, which are integral to teaching the unit. By comparing responses from the pre- and post-unit assessments, you will be able to document both individual and class learning. The post-unit assessment is on pg. 193, following Lesson 16.

It is best not to present the pre-unit assessment as a test and not to grade the responses. Remember that students' responses now may be short and limited, but you should see some real growth in their answers by the end of the unit.

Brainstorming Session

During the brainstorming session, listen for how much students know about the following:

■ Complex relationships exist in an environment.

■ Plants produce their own food.

■ Plants are at the beginning of the food chain.

■ Some animals depend on plants and/or animals for their food.

Students may or may not mention more complex issues, such as the following:

■ Living things may depend on nonliving things for their shelter.

■ Living things include not only plants and animals but also microorganisms.

Students will revisit this list as part of a post-unit assessment and will have the opportunity to evaluate their own growth.

Notebook Entries

In the individual notebook entries, you can assess students' baseline knowledge by looking for the following:

■ An attempt to describe the complexity of the relationships, including those that pertain to food, shelter, and safety from predators

■ A vocabulary that indicates a familiarity with the interdependent relationships that exist in an environment

Students may or may not mention more complicated issues, such as the following:

■ Ecosystems existed naturally, without human disruption, for a very long time, and still can.

■ Both natural occurrences and human interferences can upset the stability in an ecosystem.

Throughout the unit, students will record what they are learning in their science notebooks or on record sheets. By comparing these entries at different times, you will be able to assess individual growth.

Notes

■ If you have not already done so, prepare the bottles according to the directions in Preparing the Bottles, on pg. 18. Decide how you will involve your students in this process and proceed with your plan before going on to Lesson 2.

■ If you have not already done so, order the living materials that will be used in Lessons 3, 4, and 6. See the Unit Time Line (pg. 9) and Ordering Live Materials (pg. 6) for more information on the ordering process. Remember that Carolina Biological Supply Company must receive each card at least 20 business days before your requested delivery date. Also, remember that the live materials for Lesson 6 can be delivered on a different date from the live materials for Lessons 3 and 4. Use your time line to plan your arrival dates.

The Riverbank Environment

Setting Up the Terrarium

Overview and Objectives

Building on students' discussions of the riverbank environment and observations of their own environment in Lesson 1, students now brainstorm ways in which living things in an environment depend on one another. This lesson also introduces students to the process of using a model for making scientific observations. By constructing model terraria and beginning a written record of the components, students begin to think about the relationships among living and nonliving things. Their discussions about the terraria provide a basis for thinking about the aquaria they will set up in Lesson 3.

- Students share what they know about a terrestrial environment.

- Students think about the aquaria and terraria as models of environments.

- Students set up their terraria.

- Students make detailed records about the items they have placed in the terraria.

- Students predict what will happen in their terraria in the next week.

Background

Just as the earth is made up of land and water, so will the ecocolumns contain these two elements. The upper portion, which the students will begin making today, will be the terrarium (from the Latin *terra*, which means "land"). The terrarium will include living terrestrial plants and animals appropriate to a land environment, as well as some nonliving materials.

The lower portion will be the aquarium (from the Latin word *aqua*, which means "water"). Composed of living aquatic organisms, as well as some nonliving materials, it will represent a pond ecosystem.

The terraria will thrive only if students plant correctly today. So, it is important that you stress the need to follow directions. Planting the seeds too deeply will delay germination; planting too many will cause overcrowding.

Remember that it is very important for student volunteers to plant seeds in the seven class terraria, which will be used in the pollution experiments in Lessons 11 and on. Although the class volunteers will be responsible for planting, watering, and maintaining the class terraria, remind the entire class to observe the plant growth in these seven terraria.

After students plant in their terraria, they will build and study aquaria. This will give the terraria plants a chance to grow before the animals are added. If the plants do not have sufficient time to grow, there will be no food source for the animals and they will die. Also, if added immediately, the animals might eat the seeds prior to germination, reducing plant life considerably. Students should continue to make observations in their terraria while they are building the aquaria.

Since observation is one of the key skills students will develop in this unit, it is useful for you to note their observational abilities from the very beginning. Keep in mind that some students may not have highly developed observation skills, so you can expect their initial attempts to be somewhat vague and imprecise.

You can help students focus their observations by having them use a hand lens. Two effective ways to use the lenses are

- Place the lens close to your eye. Hold the object in your other hand and move it back and forth slowly until it is in focus.

- Hold the object stationary while keeping the hand lens above the object, as shown in Figure 2-1. Move the magnifier back and forth to focus.

Figure 2-1

Using a hand lens

Management Tip: Before you begin this lesson, students will need to have collected leaf matter, twigs, and rocks to place in their terraria today (see Final Activities Step 2, in the previous lesson). If students have not yet done this, you may want to spend the first 10 minutes of the lesson conducting this activity.

Materials

For each student
1   science notebook
1   **Record Sheet 2-A: Setting Up the Terrarium with Plants**

For every two students
1   bottle part T
1   bottle cap
3   plastic cups (one to hold a cup of gravel and then water, another to serve as the base for the terrarium, and one to hold the two cupfuls of soil)

2 cupfuls of soil

1 piece of fiberglass screen, about 10 cm (4 in) square

1 rubber band

1 spoon

1 cupful of water

1 dropper

1 cupful of gravel

1 30-ml (1-oz) cup of each seed type: grass, alfalfa, and mustard seeds (each cup contains 20–30 of one seed type)

2 toothpicks

1 hand lens

1 fine-point permanent marker

Leaf matter, small rock, twigs collected by students

For the class

Newspaper to protect tables and desks

Cleanup supplies: whisk broom and pan, sponges or rags, paper towels, pan of water

Note: Each of the seven class terraria requires the same materials listed above in the section "For every two students." Solicit volunteers to build the class terraria in their spare time before the next lesson.

Preparation

1. Make certain that all bottles, including the bottles for the seven class eco-columns, are prepared. Use the directions in Preparing the Bottles, on pg. 20.

2. Place 20 to 30 grass seeds into each 30-ml cup. Repeat for the alfalfa and mustard seeds. Make sure you have enough of each seed type for every two students.

3. Set out materials "cafeteria style" for easy pickup (see Figure 2-2 for a possible distribution center). These guidelines may help you organize your distribution center efficiently.

   ■ Select an area of the room where students can easily walk by in single file on both sides of the supplies.

   ■ Position all the materials in a line on a series of desks or tables, or on the floor, if necessary.

   ■ Place a label on each item telling students what it is and how much to take.

4. Establish a cleanup area. Supply it with sponges, paper towels or rags, a plastic-lined trash can, and a pan of water.

5. Moisten the soil slightly if it is too dry and loose.

6. Duplicate **Record Sheet 2-A: Setting Up the Terrarium.**

Management Tip: Record sheets have been provided throughout the unit. You can duplicate the record sheets for students or have students use the record sheets as models to record observations in their science notebooks. Throughout the unit, students will need to record daily observations, and the record sheets will accommodate only the first day's observations. Ask your students how they can expand on this model to create a table they can use over several days.

Figure 2-2

Distribution center

7. Revisit the riverbank environment to find some concrete examples of living and nonliving things for the discussion in this lesson's **Final Activities.**

8. Select volunteers to set up the seven class terraria. Remind the students to maintain these terraria throughout the unit.

Procedure

1. Ask students to think about their exploration of the school or home environments. Have them discuss questions such as the following:

   ■ What organisms live in the environment?

   ■ How do the animals depend on the plants for their needs? How do the plants depend on the animals?

   ■ How do the plants depend on microorganisms in the soil?

   ■ What nonliving things do the plants and animals depend on?

   ■ How did the living things you observed get food, shelter, water, and protection?

2. To set the stage for today's lesson, hold a brief discussion on these questions:

   ■ What is a terrarium? What is an aquarium? (You might tell the students the Latin roots if this seems appropriate.)

   ■ Does anyone in the class have an aquarium or terrarium at home? What do they contain?

   ■ Why did we prepare these bottles?

   ■ What do you think will go into them?

3. Let students know that today they are going to begin building their terraria. Go over the instructions on how to set up a terrarium (pgs. 44–45 of this guide and pgs. 11–12 of the Student Activity Book). Solicit class volunteers who will build the seven class terraria.

4. Distribute **Record Sheet 2-A** (or use it as a model for recordkeeping in science notebooks) and go over it with the class. Ask students why accurate scientific observations with labeled drawings are important.

5. Introduce students to the distribution center and explain how they are to pick up their supplies. If necessary, model the procedure for them. Emphasize that they need to be patient, wait their turns, and follow the directions on the table to gather what they need.

6. Show the students all of the cleanup supplies. Establish routines for independent cleanup.

7. Let students work at their own pace to set up the terraria. Circulate around the room to check on planting techniques and to remind students to record what they are putting in the terraria as they proceed. Encourage them to use their hand lenses to look at the seeds, soil, twigs, leaf matter, and rock as they work with each one.

Management Tip: Germinating seeds must be kept moist. Remind students to water gently with the droppers when the soil's surface appears dry. Unless your classroom is unusually dry, plan to water twice a week. Remind students to remove the terrarium cap each time they water. That way, they can count how many dropperfuls of water the terrarium needs before water drips through the bottom of the bottle. Knowing this number is vital to Lesson 11's pollution experiment.

8. As teams finish, ask them to return materials to the distribution center and clean up:

   ■ Return materials to the distribution center.

   ■ Dispose of trash.

   ■ Wipe off wet surfaces.

   ■ Clean the droppers, cups, and other containers. Remind students not to use soap, since it may harm the live materials involved.

9. Ask students where the best place to store the terraria might be and why (a fairly warm location with plenty of light, since seeds need warmth to germinate and light once they have sprouted).

Final Activities

1. Ask students to predict in their notebooks what they think will happen in their terraria in the next week or so. Then have them share predictions with the class. You may want to use the following questions to guide the discussion:

   ■ Which seeds do you think will germinate (sprout) first?

   ■ What will the sprouts look like?

   ■ Do you think every seed will germinate?

   ■ Will the dead plant material change? Will the rock change?

   ■ Why will these plants be important to the terrarium once we add animals to it?

2. Let students know that in the next lesson they will begin adding both living and nonliving materials to the aquarium section of their ecocolumns.

   Note: The student volunteers who are maintaining the seven class ecocolumns will be adding only plants and nonliving materials to their aquaria.

3. Invite students to think about what kinds of creatures might stay healthy in the limited space of an aquarium. Using the riverbank environment illustration to help focus the discussion, ask the following questions:

   ■ What kinds of organisms might we find in a real pond?

   ■ What are some of the things that water plants need in order to grow well?

   ■ How do plants help the animals in a pond?

   ■ What kinds of nonliving materials would we find in an aquatic environment?

4. Remind students to continue to observe and keep records on their terraria and the seven class terraria every day and to record the number of dropperfuls used to water each one.

Management Tip: To begin building the aquaria in Lesson 4, you will need approximately 25 liters (4 to 5 gal) of prepared water (see Appendix A, pg. 213).

Extensions

┌─────────────────┐
│ **MATHEMATICS** │
└─────────────────┘

1. In about a week to 10 days, germination should be complete. Have students estimate the percentage of seeds that germinated in their terraria. Did one kind of seed have a higher germination rate than the other two? You may also determine a class mode or median.

┌─────────────┐
│ **SCIENCE** │
└─────────────┘

2. Have students carry out some simple germination experiments. They can use seeds from their lunch (apple, orange, peach, cherry), from the playground (acorn, dandelion, grass, maple), or from the grocery store (lima bean, mung bean). Ask them to investigate a particular question, such as, Will seeds germinate faster in the light or in the dark? Or, they can simply lay the seeds on wet paper towels or sponges to see what sprouts.

┌───────────────────┐
│ **LANGUAGE ARTS** │
└───────────────────┘

3. The Latin word for "land," *terra,* is the root for a number of English words, such as terrarium and terrier (small dogs who dig into the earth to hunt and drive out game). Challenge your class to come up with a list of land-related *terra* words.

Assessment

1. In Lessons 2 through 13, use the following criteria to evaluate your students' growth in making and recording observations.

   ■ Clarity. Are descriptions clear and precise? Have students included dates? Is the information well organized?

   ■ Completeness. Have students described in detail all elements of the environment?

- Accuracy. Have they recorded specific measurements, or have they used general terms (such as "long") to record measurements? Is what you see on paper close to the real thing? Some students may draw stereotyped pictures, which may show what they think the item ought to look like, while others will attempt to draw the actual item. Have they labeled their drawings?

- Vocabulary. Have students been able to incorporate newly acquired words into their written observations?

- Forming hypotheses. Have they explained why things are happening and changing or made predictions about the changes that might occur?

2. For the remainder of the unit, look for growth in the following areas:

- Making detailed observations and descriptions

- Using observations to support statements

- Taking responsibility in caring for organisms

Student Instructions for Setting Up the Terrarium

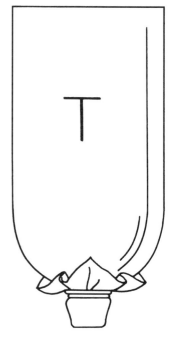

1. Use part T for the terrarium.

2. Remove the cap from part T. (Save the cap. You will be using it again at the end of this lesson.) Place a square piece of fiberglass screen over the mouth of the bottle. Secure the screen with a rubber band. Place the band on the neck of the bottle to hold the piece of screen in place.

3. Stand part T, neck down, on a plastic cup. One partner will need to hold the terrarium steady. The other can put in the things. Be sure to take turns doing this.

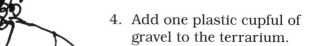

4. Add one plastic cupful of gravel to the terrarium.

5. Add two plastic cupfuls of soil on top of the gravel. Try not to muddy the sides of the terrarium as you work.

6. Divide the surface of the terrarium soil into four equal parts. (You can use your toothpick to draw the dividing lines in the soil.) Each part will hold something different. Since the soil will not stay divided permanently, use a marking pen to label the outside of the bottle with the words "leaf matter" and the names of all three seeds. This will help you remember where each type of seed was planted.

7. In three of the parts you will plant seeds. Plant all three kinds the same way:

- First, count your alfalfa seeds, and record the number. Use the hand lens to observe the seeds. Sprinkle the seeds evenly on the soil's surface in their proper section. Use your toothpick or a pencil tip to spread them out if necessary. Press them down **gently** with your fingers. **Be careful not to plant too deeply.**

- When you have planted all the alfalfa seeds in their proper section, plant the grass and mustard seeds the same way in their own sections.

- Use your empty gravel cup to get one cup of water. With the water dropper, wet the soil thoroughly. Count how many droppers of water your terrarium will take before the water begins to drip out of the bottom. Record this number on **Record Sheet 2-A: Setting Up the Terrarium** or in your science notebook. Now replace the bottle cap to prevent leaks.

- Decide how many times a week you will water your terrarium. Remove the cap each time and replace it once the water drips through. Record the number of water drops each time you water your plants. The number of drops must be accurate. It is important to know how much liquid the soil in your terrarium will hold before it begins to leak. You will use this information later in the unit.

8. In the fourth section, add some dead plant material, like leaf matter and a new twig or two. A small rock would fit nicely, too. Use a hand lens to observe these materials.

9. On **Record Sheet 2-A** or in your science notebook, draw and label a picture of what you put in your terrarium. Include information on how many seeds you planted, what the dead plant material is and looks like, and what the rock looks like.

10. Plan to make daily observations of your terrarium and record this information in your science notebook. Remember to observe the sides of your terrarium for any changes that may be occurring in the soil.

Record Sheet 2-A

Name: _____

Date: _____

Setting Up the Terrarium

Use this table to record how you set up your terrarium today. Take time to observe each item closely with the hand lens.

Observe changes in your terrarium each day throughout this unit. Record these daily observations in your science notebook. You may want to use this table as a model. Be certain to include dates for each observation.

1. Fill in the table.

Terrarium Observations Table

	Amount and Size	Color/ Description	Other Observations (for example, texture and shape)
Soil (including gravel)			
Alfalfa Seed			
Grass Seed			
Mustard Seed			
Rock			
Twig			
Dead Leaves			
Water			

Record Sheet 2-A

Name: _____

Setting Up the Terrarium *(continued)*

2. In this circle, draw and label your terrarium as it looks from above.

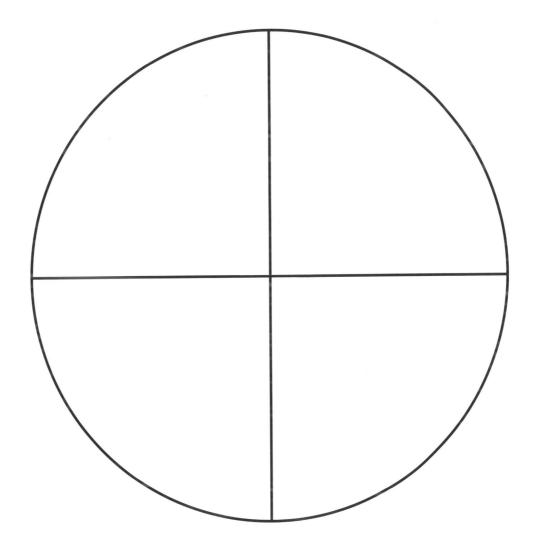

Setting Up the Aquarium

Overview and Objectives

In Lesson 2, students began building an understanding of how living things depend on one another. Lesson 3 extends their thinking from land to aquatic environments. As the class shares observations of the terraria and aquaria, students learn to verify and challenge statements using their own observations, a process skill they continue to practice throughout the unit. After carefully observing the elodea, duckweed, and algae firsthand, students use a series of reading selections to discover more about these organisms and the roles they play in maintaining the ecosystem.

- Students discuss the needs of organisms in an aquatic environment.
- Students set up their aquaria by adding gravel, water, elodea, duckweed, and algae.
- Students observe, quantify, and record information about the organisms they place in their aquaria.
- Students read about the role of plants and algae in a pond.

Background

Each of the types of aquatic producers that students place in their aquaria play a vital role in maintaining the ecosystem. The plants and algae in the aquarium get dissolved nutrients from the aquarium sediment, take in carbon dioxide and produce oxygen, and provide young fish with food and a hiding place from predators. To understand these roles in later lessons, students need to observe these organisms carefully and read about them.

Reading selections on the aquarium producers appear at the end of this lesson and on pg. 17 in the Student Activity Book. While the readings offer useful background information, have students wait until they have had enough time to make their own observations before reading them. Research shows that students retain written information better when it follows hands-on experience. You can assign it for homework, during language arts, or during your students' free time at school.

A three-day break is scheduled between Lessons 3 and 4 to enable students to observe the elodea, duckweed, and algae in their aquaria. This is a good time for student volunteers to add these organisms to the seven class aquaria.

Materials

For each student

1   science notebook
1   **Record Sheet 3-A: Setting Up the Aquarium**

For every two students

1   terrarium from previous lesson
1   bottle part A
1½ liters of water (See Appendix A)
2   300-ml (10-oz) clear plastic cups (one cup holds gravel and then water; the other holds algae)
1   300-ml (10-oz) plastic cup of gravel
2   paper towels
1 or 2   sprigs of elodea
10–15   duckweed plants
3   dropperfuls of algae
1   dropper
1   hand lens
1   spoon
1   metric ruler

For the class

1 or 2   sheets of newsprint
1   marker
    Prepared water
    Newspaper to protect tabletops and desks
    Cleanup supplies

Note: Additional materials are needed to create the seven class aquaria. Solicit volunteers to build the aquaria in their spare time before Lesson 4. Each of the seven class aquaria requires the same materials listed above in the section "For every two students."

Preparation

1. If you have not yet done so, prepare the water students will put in their aquaria. See Appendix A for more information.

2. Rinse the gravel thoroughly in prepared water so dust does not make the water cloudy.

3. Wet the paper towels, fan them so they can be picked up easily, and stack them in a pile so they will not dry out. Each pair of students will get two paper towels.

4. Set out materials "cafeteria style" for easy pickup (see Figure 3-1). Remove the lids from the algae jars. Students will use their own droppers to take the algae directly from the jars.

5. Establish a cleanup area.

6. Duplicate one copy of **Record Sheet 3-A** for each student, or use it as a model.

7. Title a sheet of newsprint "What Do Aquatic Organisms Need?" Hang it where you can record student ideas during the opening discussion.

8. Put out the seven class terraria.

Figure 3-1

Distribution center

Procedure

1. Have students pick up their terraria and hand lenses. Remind them to use the lenses to observe any changes that may be occurring in their own terraria, as well as in the seven class terraria. Discuss the following questions. Focus on both the students' and the class terraria.

   ■ What changes do you observe in your terrarium?

   ■ What are some signs that your seeds are beginning to germinate and grow?

   ■ Are there any changes above the soil? Look through the sides of the terrarium. Are there any changes taking place in the soil?

   ■ Are there any changes in the nonliving materials?

   ■ From your observations, what do you predict will happen in your terrarium in the next day, the next week, and the next two weeks?

   ■ Do you know how often your team should water your terrarium? How much water do you think it will need each time? Why?

2. Ask students to share their ideas about the question, What do aquatic organisms need? Use the newsprint to record their ideas. The following questions may help focus the discussion:

   ■ What do plants need to live?

   ■ What do algae need to live?

   ■ What do animals need to live?

   ■ Think of one living thing. How does it get what it needs to live in nature?

   ■ How will we provide for these needs in an aquarium?

3. Review with the class the **Student Instructions for Setting Up the Aquarium** on pg. 54 of this guide and on pg. 16 of the Student Activity Book.

4. Distribute **Record Sheet 3-A** and go over it with the class. Review the importance of accurate, scientific drawings—they should be large, clear, labeled, and detailed. Let the students know the capacity of the plastic cups (300 ml or 10 oz) so they can record the amounts of water and gravel on their record sheets.

5. Review how students are to pick up their supplies and live materials from the distribution center.

Management Tips

■ If the water at the distribution center is not in pre-measured 1½-liter containers (one for each pair of students), then each team must use a 300-ml (10-oz) cup to measure the water needed to fill their aquaria.

■ As students go through the distribution center, they should use the two wet paper towels to hold the elodea and duckweed. Emphasize that these are living plants and should be handled gently. They should not be out of water for long. Have students use their second cup to hold the three dropperfuls of algae.

■ Make certain that students take only the amount of duckweed and algae listed on the student instructions. Too much duckweed and algae could choke out the aquaria's animal life. Because the duckweed are so small, they are difficult to measure at first. Help students estimate.

6. Now let students set up their aquaria. Circulate around the room asking questions and assisting where needed.

7. When teams have finished setting up the aquaria, ask them to help clean up.

8. Involve students in the decision regarding the best place to store the aquaria.

Note: The aquatic plants and algae in this unit need plenty of bright light and a moderate (room) temperature (23°C to 25°C, or 73°F to 77°F). When choosing a location for the aquaria, avoid drafty areas, heating or cooling vents, and places with strong direct sunlight, such as window sills. Also consider a place easily accessible for observations.

9. Remind students that cleanup is their responsibility.

Final Activities

1. Discuss why it is important to add plants and algae to the aquaria. Have students compare these answers with why it is important to have plants in a terrarium.

2. After students have had a chance to observe their own (and the class) aquaria and record these observations, ask students to read "Duckweed, Elodea, and Algae: Why are They Important?" beginning on pg. 17 of the Student Activity Book (pg. 55 of this guide). Have them look for reasons why plants and algae are important in an aquarium.

Management Tip: Remind students to record daily observations of their terraria, including how many dropperfuls of water their terraria can absorb before the water flows out of the base.

3. Ask students to write in their notebooks three ideas about what they have read.

Extensions

SCIENCE **LANGUAGE ARTS**

1. Hundreds of interesting plants live in and around ponds: water lilies, cattails, irises, horsetails, and arrowheads, to name just a few. Ask students to choose one, do some library research about its life cycle, and draw it. They can then share what they learned with the class.

SCIENCE

2. Ask students to add some more nonliving things to the aquaria, such as rocks or twigs. Have students rinse these things in prepared water before adding them. Make sure students understand not to add more living things, since these could alter the results of experiments in later lessons.

SCIENCE

3. Invite students to choose a plant that grows in the school yard, neighborhood, local park, or backyard, or one that thrives in a local watery environment. Have them observe the plant carefully, then ask them to do the following:

   ■ List the ways the plant is similar to elodea.

   ■ List the ways in which the plant is different from elodea.

   ■ Have students make the same comparisons between their new plant and duckweed.

LANGUAGE ARTS

4. Challenge students to compile a list of water words containing the Latin root word *aqua*.

MATHEMATICS

5. Ask students to estimate how many of the cups they used in this lesson could be filled from a 1-liter bottle of soda? A 2-liter bottle?

Notes
■ Schedule a three-day break between Lessons 3 and 4.
■ Do not connect the aquaria and terraria yet. This will encourage students to observe each part separately. They will join the two systems in Lesson 7.

Student Instructions for Setting Up the Aquarium

1. Use part A for your aquarium.

2. Put one cupful of gravel in the bottom of the aquarium.

3. Use your empty gravel cup to fill your aquarium with water until it is approximately three to four cm from the top. (Be careful. If the water is too high, it may overflow when you join the aquarium and terrarium.)

4. Record how many cupfuls of water you used to fill your aquarium. Mark the water line on the bottle.

5. Add the elodea, duckweed, and algae. Carefully measure out the amount of each organism as instructed below, since too much duckweed and algae may choke out the animal life in your aquarium.

- **1 or 2 sprigs of elodea**

   Place the elodea on a wet paper towel.

   Measure the plant and record its size.

   Place the plant in the aquarium.

   Plant it in the gravel or let it float freely.

- **10 to 15 duckweed plants**

   Use your spoon to scoop up the tiny plants and put them onto your wet paper towel. (Hint: Since they are so small, estimate the numbers.)

   Put the plants in the aquarium.

   Count the plants and record the number. (You can record a more exact count once they are in your aquarium, since duckweed will separate when floating.)

- **3 dropperfuls of algae**

   Use your dropper and place 3 dropperfuls of algae into your cup.

   Can you see the algae in the jars? Record what you see on your record sheet or in your notebook.

   Put the algae into your aquarium. Record what you see.

6. Then draw and label a picture of how your aquarium looks today. Use your hand lens to observe closely.

7. Observe your aquarium every day throughout the rest of the unit. Use your science notebook to record these daily observations. Make certain you include any changes.

Reading Selection

Duckweed, Elodea, and Algae: Why Are They Important?

Why should you add duckweed, elodea, and algae to your aquarium? Each is special in its own way. Water plants, like elodea and duckweed, are beautiful to look at. Algae and water plants help keep a healthy exchange of gas in the water. They also provide food and shelter for many animals. What other reasons can you think of for adding these organisms to your aquarium?

Not Just Beautiful to Look At

Aquatic organisms such as duckweed, elodea, and algae add a special kind of beauty to our world. Some have bright colors and unusual shapes. Others sway with the gentle motion of the water's current.

These producers are especially important in a pond or slow-moving stream. This is because they help provide oxygen for animals in the water. How? By taking in one gas (carbon dioxide, or CO_2) and giving off another (oxygen or O_2).

Some aquatic organisms provide homes and protection for tinier organisms and baby animals. These creatures nestle in the leaves and stems of underwater plants where they can live safely.

Why Swap Gases?

Animals, plants, and other living things, such as algae and bacteria, are always using oxygen. This is called **respiration.** Respiration helps organisms get energy. In the daylight, organisms that have chlorophyll, such as plants, algae, and some bacteria, can use the sun's energy, water, and carbon dioxide to make their own food. We call this **photosynthesis.** Through photosynthesis, these organisms release much more oxygen than they take in. In the water, animals such as fish, snails, and tadpoles use the oxygen to breathe.

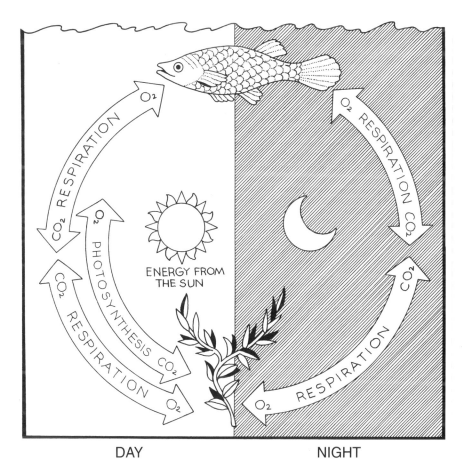

Oxygen-carbon dioxide cycle

From Moose to Flea

Water plants and algae also provide food for many animals, from the huge moose to the tiny water flea. Because green plants and algae carry on photosynthesis to produce their own food, they are called **producers.** Producers make the food that animals need to live. Since animals cannot produce their own food, they must eat other organisms to get energy. This is why animals, such as the moose and tiny water flea, are known as **consumers.** They eat, or consume, water plants and algae, such as those you will find in your ecocolumns.

Let's take a look at each of these producers now.

Water flea magnified

Water plants and algae are food for the huge moose and tiny flea.

Where There Is Water, There Are Algae

Thousands of kinds of algae live in every wet environment you can think of. They come in all sizes, from microscopic (like the kind you will be growing) to gigantic (like the 46-m-long [150-ft-long] brown kelp). They also come in a rainbow of colors: green, golden, brown, and red.

Microscopic algae are too small to see with just your eyes. But if you've ever seen a pond with what looks like green water, you've seen algae by the millions. It's actually the algae that turn the water green. But you can see them only when they grow in great numbers.

Duckweed: Food for Fowl

Duckweed is a tiny floating plant. It usually grows on the surfaces of ponds, lakes, and slow-moving streams. Duckweed is a favorite food of many waterfowl—ducks, for instance—which is how it got its name. Fish and snails eat duckweed, too.

When growing conditions are good, duckweed plants will multiply very rapidly and form a lush carpet on the top of the water. This thick covering is lovely to look at. But it can cut off so much light from other water plants that it can kill them. That means there is less life-giving oxygen in the water.

Healthy duckweed is bright yellow-green. It is an unusual plant because it has no leaves or stems. Instead, it consists of one to three leaflike fronds attached at the center. From each frond a single root hangs. Use your hand lens to observe one duckweed plant up close.

DUCKWEED

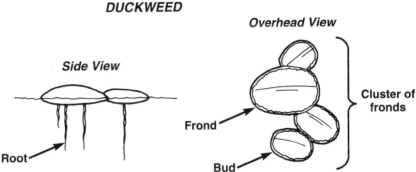

Make New Fronds

Duckweed rarely flowers, and it almost never does out of nature. So how does duckweed make new plants? It buds to form new fronds. Each frond grows its own root and then becomes an independent plant. In nature we usually can't observe a single frond of duckweed; the fronds tend to stay in groups until four or more plants are produced. (That is why it may have been difficult for you to count out 10 to 15 duckweed plants when setting up your aquarium.)

Why do you think they call it "duckweed"?

Elodea: A Well-Adapted Plant

Elodea is a dark green plant. It's found in ponds and slow-moving streams. Elodea has pointed leaves. And the leaves grow around the stem in tight whorls, or circles, of three or more. These leaves provide excellent shelter for baby fish. The stem itself is kind of brittle. Still, it can grow up to two feet long. Along this stem, new branches often grow.

You will find elodea interesting to observe in your aquarium. It is able to grow in two ways. It can float freely near the surface of the water. Or, it can take root at the bottom. You may notice free-floating plants sending down long pale roots.

What happens when elodea breaks apart into smaller segments? Each piece can grow into a new plant. And like its parent, each new plant can either float or take root.

Easy to Grow

Elodea is very hardy and easy to grow. It thrives in strong light. But it can survive for a fairly long time in low light, too. If there is not much light, the plant will become thin. It may lose some of its bright color. If you put it back in bright light, though, it will grow strong again.

All of these features are adaptive. They help the plant survive under poor conditions. But they can also make the plant a problem for people, animals, and other plants. Can you imagine why? Well, first because elodea grows so quickly it can clog waterways. It can also crowd out other plant life on both the water's top and bottom.

Your aquarium has only three types of producers. But real waterways, such as oceans, ponds, and streams, have a wide variety. Can you name some others?

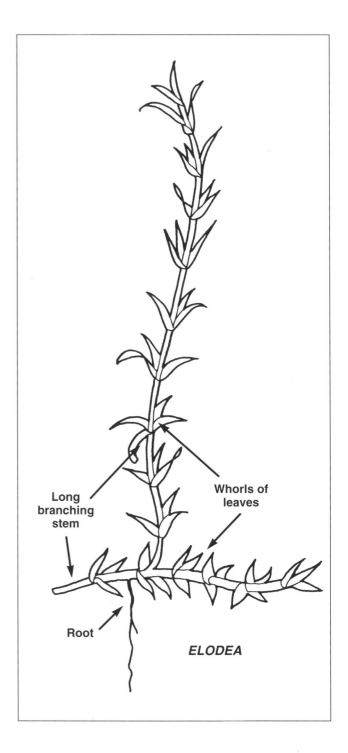

Long branching stem

Whorls of leaves

Root

ELODEA

Record Sheet 3-A

Name: _____

Date: _____

Setting Up the Aquarium

Use this table to record today's observations of your aquarium. Take the time to observe closely with the hand lens. Record what you see as accurately and completely as possible.

1. Fill in this table.

Observations Table

	Amount and Size	Color/ Description	Other Observations (for example, texture and shape)
Gravel			
Water			
Elodea			
Duckweed			
Algae			

Record Sheet 3-A   Name: _____

Setting Up the Aquarium *(continued)*

2. Draw the contents of your aquarium in this bottle. Be sure to label every item.

Adding Animals to the Aquarium

Overview and Objectives

Students have now observed, discussed, and read about duckweed, elodea, and algae and have been introduced to the idea that green plants and algae make their own food. Building on that understanding, students shift their focus from plants and algae as producers of food to animals as consumers of food. Observing their own aquarium helps students learn that all the organisms have interdependent relationships. As they continue to explore these relationships, students will devise their own definition of the term "ecosystem."

■ Students discuss information on aquatic plants and algae gained through observation and reading.

■ Students complete their aquaria by adding mosquito fish and snails.

■ Students continue to record their observations of the plants, algae, and animals in their aquaria and the plants in their terraria.

■ Students read to learn more about the animals in their aquaria.

Background

Students will be eager to shift their attention to animals; however, it is important to keep animals out of the picture until the class has had the chance to process all their new information on plants. You need to set up the distribution center before the lesson; therefore, conceal the live materials from the students during the lesson discussion. One way to do this is to put the snails in their holding tanks on the table after the discussion is over and before distributing them. Or, simply put the tanks on the table and cover them carefully.

Be sure to caution students about handling live animals, emphasizing that these animals are fragile. Urge students to follow the directions carefully and use spoons, cups, and nets to pick up their organisms. They should avoid holding the organisms in their hands to prevent contamination and to prevent the animals from being out of water for too long.

The fish in this unit are *Gambusia*, more commonly known as "mosquito fish." The term "mosquito fish" refers to many small livebearing fish used in mosquito larvae control, including guppies. The *Gambusia* is quite similar in structure and appearance to the guppy. It is, however, a hardier fish than the guppy and can withstand a wide range of temperatures. Since the term "mosquito fish" may be easier for the students to remember, the *Gambusia* will be referred to as mosquito fish throughout the unit.

Students who maintain an aquarium at home may be concerned about how the mosquito fish will receive oxygen in an aquarium that does not have an aeration system. This aquarium is a self-contained ecosystem. The elodea, algae, and surface diffusion will provide enough oxygen. Students may periodically use their droppers to gently pump air into the tank to renew the water surface and circulate the oxygen.

The reading selections in this lesson provide information on the snail and mosquito fish. (You can use guppies rather than mosquito fish in this unit. A reading selection on guppies is provided in Appendix B.) Review the reading selections for background information on these animals. Decide if you want to assign them for homework or as part of language arts.

Note: The student volunteers who have been creating and maintaining the class aquaria and terraria will **not** be adding animals to the class aquaria in this lesson. These aquaria will be used in pollution experiments that start in Lesson 11.

Materials

For each student
- 1   science notebook
- 1   **Record Sheet 4-A: Aquarium Observations**

For every two students
- 1   terrarium (set up in Lesson 2)
- 1   aquarium (set up in Lesson 3)
- 2   medium-sized pond snails
- 2   mosquito fish
- 1   hand lens
- 1   spoon
- 1   clear plastic cup
- 1   dropper
- 1   metric ruler

For the class
- Aquarium thermometer
- 6   small dip nets
- Newspapers to protect tabletops and desks
- Cleanup supplies

Preparation

1. Duplicate **Record Sheet 4-A: Aquarium Observations.**

2. Set out materials in the distribution center for easy pickup (see Figure 4-1). Place the dip nets in each holding tank. Decide now how to handle setting out the live organisms.

3. Use the aquarium thermometer to make certain the aquarium temperatures are within three degrees of the holding tank water. If not, review Step 5 of the Student Instructions for Adding Animals to the Aquarium, on pg. 68.

4. Set out the cleanup materials.

5. This is a long lesson. Decide if you want to divide it into two parts. A possible dividing point is indicated on pg. 66.

Figure 4-1

*Distribution
center*

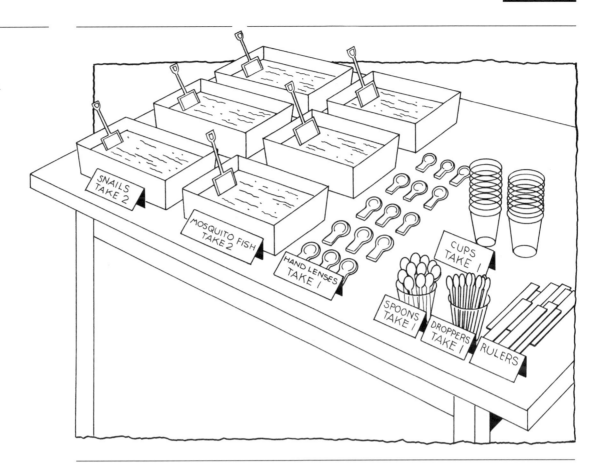

Procedure

1. Ask students to use their hand lenses to observe any changes in the terraria. Give them time to record observations and additional notes in their science notebooks. Use the following questions to guide the discussion:

   ■ Have any of your seeds germinated (sprouted)? Compare their color, length, size, and roots. Are the roots visible above or below the soil's surface?

   ■ Which plants seem to be germinating quickly? Predict what your terrarium will look like in one week on the basis of these observations.

   Management Tip: Remind students to water their terraria and to record how many dropperfuls they used.

2. Have students pick up their aquaria so that the aquatic plants and algae are in front of them during the discussion. Use the following questions to check students' thinking, keeping in mind that the main goal of this discussion is to help students begin to understand that green plants and algae can make their own food. Ask students to verify their statements with specific references to their own observations. They can refer back to the reading selection in Lesson 3 if necessary.

   ■ Describe the algae, elodea, and duckweed you placed in your aquarium. How are they alike? How are they different?

   ■ What does it mean when we say that plants and algae are producers?

   ■ What is the role of plants and algae in an aquarium?

   ■ What might happen if you were to put too many plants and algae in your aquarium? What problems could these plants and algae cause?

3. Give students time to share their notebook entries from the previous lesson's Final Activities.

4. Distribute a copy of **Record Sheet 4-A: Aquarium Observations** to each student (or use it as a model for recordkeeping in student notebooks). Have students observe their aquaria and fill out Table 1 on Record Sheet 4-A.

5. Review the Student Instructions for Adding Animals to the Aquarium, on pgs. 68–69 of this guide (pgs. 24–25 of the Student Activity Book).

6. Direct attention to the distribution center and discuss how students are to pick up their live animals today. Remind them not to touch the animals with their hands.

7. Have each team add animals to its aquarium and record observations on Table 2 on Record Sheet 4-A. Circulate around the class to help students focus their observations and, if necessary, assist students with the transfer of animals.

8. Have students mop up any spills, return supplies to the distribution center, and place the aquaria in suitable locations. The aquaria should get plenty of light for most of the day. Avoid places where the temperature fluctuates significantly.

Management Tip: If you choose to divide this lesson into two parts, this is one logical place to stop.

Final Activities

1. Allow students time to share initial observations of the aquatic animals with the class. Many students will be able to describe how the animals look, how they move, and perhaps even some of their behaviors. Stimulate the discussion with questions such as the following:

   ■ What are the similarities among all the mosquito fish? What are the differences?

   ■ What are the similarities among all the snails? What are the differences?

   ■ How are the mosquito fish and snails alike and different in the way they move? How are they different in the way they look? How do you think each of these characteristics helps the organism interact with its environment?

   ■ How does each animal contribute to the environment?

2. Briefly touch on the idea of "interdependence"—but not the term—so students can start thinking about it. (Students will come up with their own definition of interdependence in the next lesson.) The following questions may help guide the discussion:

   ■ How can we find out if animals can live without plants?

   ■ How will you know if one living thing depends on another for some of its needs?

3. Write the word "ecosystem" on the board. Ask the students, "How would you define the word 'ecosystem,' knowing that your aquarium is one type of ecosystem?" (A common response is that an ecosystem is a community of living and nonliving things that interrelate in an environment.)

4. Let students know that they will create a land ecosystem by adding animals to their own terraria, but not to the class terraria. Explain that later they will join the land and water ecosystems in an ecocolumn and observe the effect one has on the other. Ask students to predict how this land ecosystem will be similar to the water ecosystem they just created.

5. Assign the reading selections starting on pg. 26 in the Student Activity Book (pg. 70 of this guide). If you are using guppies rather than mosquito fish, make copies of the reading selection in Appendix B for your students.

6. Remind students to observe their own and the class terraria and aquaria and to record their observations.

Extensions

LANGUAGE ARTS

1. As a creative writing activity, ask students to imagine they are fish or snails. What would it be like to live in water?

ART   LANGUAGE ARTS

2. A marvelous diversity of animal life abounds in small ponds, including frogs, newts, mosquito larvae, caddisfly larvae, planarian worms, tubifex worms, turtles, mussels, diving beetles, water striders, and water boatmen. Interested students may enjoy illustrating or doing some library research on a pond dweller and sharing their information with the class.

MATHEMATICS

3. Just how slow is a snail's pace? Challenge students to find a way to measure how far their snail travels in ten minutes. At that pace, how long would it take for a snail to travel one mile?

LANGUAGE ARTS

4. Students may be eager to find out more about other aquatic environments. Challenge them to research one of these topics:

   ■ Our aquaria will be most like a pond environment. What other kinds of wet environments are there? Make a list.

   ■ Pond water is slow-moving. If you studied a fast-moving water environment, such as a mountain stream or a waterfall, how might the plants be different? How might they be the same?

Student Instructions for Adding Animals to the Aquarium

1. Dip an inch or two of water from the holding tank into your clear plastic cup.

2. Use a spoon to scoop two snails out of the holding tank into your cup.

3. At the distribution center, catch two mosquito fish in the net. Turn the net inside out and touch it to the water in order to put the fish into your cup.

4. At your work area, use your hand lens to observe the animals in the cup. Notice their size, shape, and color. Watch how they move.

5. With your dropper, move some of the water from your own aquarium to the cup. Work slowly and carefully, adding the water a little at a time until the cup is about half full. This will help your creatures get used to the water in your aquarium before you put them into it.

6. Now pour the animals gently into your aquarium.

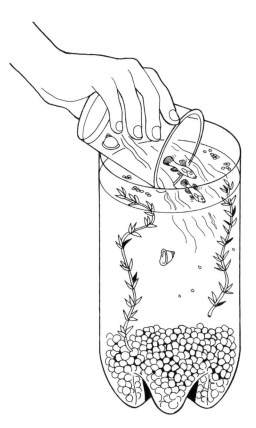

7. Use your hand lens again to observe your animals. Record your observations in Table 2. Make a new drawing of your aquarium to show how it looks today. Label everything in the drawing.

8. Observe your aquarium every day and make daily observation records in your science notebook.

Reading Selection

Mosquito Fish: Strong Little Fish

You may have seen guppies in aquaria before. But have you ever seen a **mosquito fish?** Mosquito fish look a lot like guppies. But in some ways, they are different.

Mosquito fish are strong little fish. They don't mind sudden changes or movements. They can survive a wide range of temperatures, from 4°C to 38°C (40°F to 100°F). And they can live in almost any body of fresh water—lakes, ponds, ditches, streams, and even mud holes. That's why they'll do so well in your ecocolumn.

Do you remember what *terra* meant? Think of the word "territory." Mosquito fish are very **territorial.** They will fight off other types of fish in their tank. Remember this after the unit is over.

What's in a Name?
The scientific name of the mosquito fish is *Gambusia.* It lives along the southeastern coast of the United States, in places like North Carolina.

How do you think the mosquito fish got its name? Well, feeding these fish is no problem at all. They like live food—like elodea—the best. In lakes they will eat beetles. But they are most famous for feeding on mosquito **larvae.** This immature form of mosquito wriggles around in the water. Before the larvae become adult mosquitos and can fly away, the mosquito fish eat them. This helps lower the number of mosquitos in the air. Do you know why this is important?

It's important because mosquitos can carry diseases. With fewer mosquitos, there is less chance of spreading disease. No wonder this fish has been brought into more than 70 countries throughout the world!

Who's Who?
The mosquito fish in your aquarium will be either adult males, adult females, or immature **fry** (young mosquito fish). As you observe them, try to figure out which kinds you have.

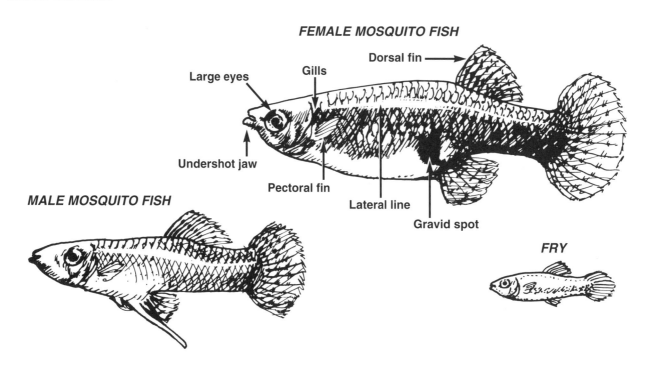

FEMALE MOSQUITO FISH

Large eyes · Gills · Dorsal fin · Undershot jaw · Pectoral fin · Lateral line · Gravid spot

MALE MOSQUITO FISH

FRY

Notice too, the characteristics all mosquito fish share:

- Their bodies are covered with protective scales that overlap like roof tiles or shingles. Use your hand lens to see them better.

- They have large round eyes and see very well.

- They have a dark line (called the **lateral line**) running the length of their bodies. The lateral line is made up of sensitive nerve endings that detect pressure in the water.

- Like all fish, they breathe by pumping water through their mouth and over their gills. How many times a minute does your fish breathe?

The adult male mosquito fish grows to a length of 3.5 cm (1½ in). He is usually a pale gray color. Sometimes he will have a faint blue color that looks like shiny metal when light hits it. His body is slim and his tail is round. The dorsal fin and tail often are marked with rows of tiny dark dots.

Females: Mosquito Fish or Guppy?
The female looks a little different from the male. She is much larger than the male and can grow up to 6 cm (2½ in) long. Like the male, she is a drab grayish blue color. But she may have a black spot on the tail. Her fins and tail are rounded, and her body is plump. Like the male, her dorsal fin and tail may have rows of tiny dark dots. The dots in the tail are the only difference between the female mosquito fish and the female guppy. Otherwise they look alike.

When the female is pregnant, her abdomen becomes very swollen. A black spot, called the **gravid spot,** appears on each side of her body just above the rear fin. She may have as few as three fry. Or, she may have over 200 at one time (but that is very rare). An average number of fry is 40 to 50.

Small Fry Head for Cover
Mosquito fish are **live-bearers.** This means their fry are born alive and fully formed. They are less than 1 cm (¼ in) at birth. They resemble females in that they are rounded and dull colored, but they are more transparent.

Can you think of a reason why dull coloring is an advantage for a baby fish? Like most live-bearers, mosquito fish like to eat their fry. To survive, the baby fish swim immediately to plants for protection (yet another reason why elodea is important to your aquarium). Then, they'll grow very quickly. Within a week or two they will be too large for their parents to swallow!

Reading Selection

Snails: A Head at the End of a Foot

Snails are found all over the globe. There are more than 1,500 kinds that live on land, 35,000 kinds in the sea, and 80,000 kinds in fresh water. Snails belong to a large class of animals called **gastropods.** This odd sounding name has an equally odd meaning: "stomach foot."

Gastropods have certain features in common. For instance, most have a soft body protected by a shell. A part of the soft body that sticks out from the shell is called the "foot." It is made mainly of muscles and helps the snail move. The snail's foot also releases a thin film of mucus. The snail glides over this film.

POND SNAIL

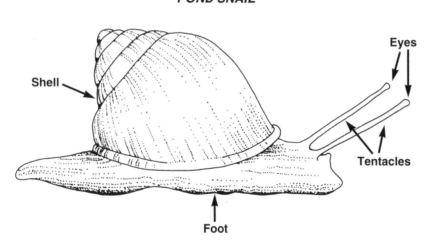

Shell

Eyes

Tentacles

Foot

Like an Antenna

The head (at the end of the foot!) has a set of tentacles with eyes. Snails can pull in these tentacles; you may be able to observe your snail moving them up and down, like a car radio antenna. The snail sees poorly. It can probably only tell the difference between light and dark. Snails are silent and cannot hear.

The snail's mouth is on the underside of the head. Look for it when your snail glides along the side of the aquarium. The mouth is a small opening that opens and closes. Inside is a tongue called a **radula.** The radula has tiny teeth that file down the snail's food into bits.

Looking for Baby Snails

Most snails reproduce by laying eggs. You may be lucky enough to find some in your own aquarium. Examine the plants and the sides of the aquarium. Do you see a small jellylike mass containing tiny, developing snails? Look carefully close to the water line. Use a hand lens to watch them grow inside the "jelly" for a week or two. Then they will simply walk out, little copies of their parents.

As the baby snail's soft body grows, its outer shell does, too. The snail makes its own shell, much the same way you make your own fingernails. To do this, the snail needs calcium from the environment. (Why do you think it's important for you to drink milk?) Inside the snail's body, an organ called the **mantle** secretes the shell.

Pond snails are **scavengers.** They eat the soft tissues of dead plants and animals. You might call them the "cleanup crew" of their environment. Pond snails also will eat algae and live plants. In turn, snails are food for fish, turtles, ducks, large insects, and mammals.

Record Sheet 4-A

Name: _____

Date: _____

Aquarium Observations

Record today's observations of your aquarium. Use a hand lens to observe closely. Then, record what you see as accurately and completely as you can.

1. Record observations on your aquarium plants and algae below. Note any changes that have occurred since the last time you observed.

Table 1

	Observations	What Has Changed?
Elodea		
Duckweed		
Algae		

Record Sheet 4-A   Name: _____

Aquarium Observations *(continued)*

2. Record observations of your animals.

Table 2

	Snails	Mosquito Fish
Size		
Number		
Color		
Motion		
Shape		
Other		

Record Sheet 4-A   Name: _____

Aquarium Observations *(continued)*

3. In the space below, draw and label your aquarium and everything in it.

4. Observe your aquarium every day. Place your daily observations in your science notebook.

Observing the Completed Aquarium

Overview and Objectives

In Lesson 4, students discussed that an "ecosystem" is a community of living and nonliving things interrelated in an environment. With this concept in mind, students now develop their own meaning of the term "interdependence." Through a class webbing activity, students synthesize what they have read and observed about aquatic ecosystems. In writing, students then focus on the dependent and interdependent relationships in their ecosystems to identify observable evidence that these relationships really do exist.

- Students discuss what they have read and observed about the animals in their aquaria.

- Students offer evidence of the dependent and interdependent relationships they have observed in their own ecosystems.

- Students predict what changes might occur in both their own aquaria and terraria and in the class ones.

- Students read about germination, which they have been observing over the past week or so.

Background

This lesson enables students to grapple with the idea of dependent and interdependent relationships in an ecosystem. Since much of their understanding will come through direct observation, it is important to help students focus their observations and to guide them toward discovering these relationships firsthand in the aquaria. For example, your students may realize that certain dependent relationships exist, such as the following:

- **Gravel/plant**

  Gravel provides a base into which plant roots can grow.

- **Live organisms/water**

  All of the live organisms in the aquaria (mosquito fish, snails, elodea, algae, and duckweed) need water to survive.

  Your students may also recognize interdependent relationships, such as the following:

- **Snail/plant**

  As a producer, the plant provides food for the snail. It also offers shelter and adds some oxygen to the water. What the snail does for the plant is less obvious. In some ways, the snail is a gardener. It eats up the dead leaves (as well as some live ones, of course) and adds fertilizer in the form of feces. The snail also gives off carbon dioxide, which the plants use. However, this is not something students can observe.

■ **Fish/plant**

This relationship is nearly identical to that of the snail and the plant, except that fish prefer to eat live plant material.

■ **Gravel/plant**

This relationship, though more dependent, can also be seen as interdependent, especially in larger ecosystems such as the riverbank environment. Plant roots often hold dirt and gravel in place and prevent the dirt or gravel from washing away. The gravel holds the plant in place and gives it a place to root.

In this lesson, you will use a teacher-directed webbing activity to help students visualize the relationships they have observed in their aquaria. Save the web the class generates. You will need it again in Lesson 7.

Students also will predict what other events might occur in the ecosystems. Reading selections on the life cycles of their plants, algae, and animals have given them some facts on which to base their predictions. For example, they may remember that snails lay eggs in jelly capsules, mosquito fish give birth to live babies, algae multiply and make the water look green, duckweed grows new fronds, and elodea branches and sends down roots.

If a student makes a prediction about death, acknowledge that it is a real possibility. In addition, acknowledge that students have already developed attachments to the living creatures in their ecosystems and that they will be sad if any die. Try to help students see that death is a natural part of the life cycle. In nature nothing is wasted, not even dead materials, which (when decomposed) free up nutrients in the ecosystem.

Materials

For each student

   1   science notebook

For every two students

   1   aquarium
   1   hand lens

For the class

   1   sheet of newsprint or transparency film
        Markers

Preparation

Obtain the materials for recording student ideas.

Management Tip: Remember not to use the chalkboard for the webbing activity, since you will need to refer to this class web in an upcoming lesson.

Procedure

1. Have students pick up their aquaria and hand lenses so that they can refer to their ecosystems during the class discussion.

2. Give students time to make informal observations on their own. Then invite them to share what they have learned about their aquatic ecosystems through observations and readings. Remind them to verify other classmates' observations by looking for similar evidence in their own aquaria.

3. Explain that to help students visualize the relationships in their aquaria, you will record their observations in a special way known as webbing.

   ■ To begin the web, write the main topic, "Aquarium," in the center of the sheet.

   ■ Let students know that they will discuss both living and nonliving things in the aquarium and how they depend on each other. Then add the words "living" and "nonliving" to the web as illustrated in Figure 5-1.

Figure 5-1

Starting the aquarium web

■ Elicit details from the students and add them to the web. For clarity, have students subdivide the living things into plants, algae, and animals. Then they can list each one under its proper subdivision. For an example, see Figure 5-2.

Figure 5-2

Example of expanded aquarium web

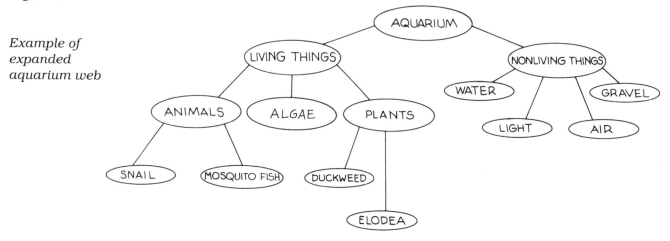

■ Continue to expand the web until every element (both living and nonliving) in the ecosystem has been included.

■ Now help students visualize the concepts of dependence and interdependence in the aquarium. Start with the nonliving elements. Ask, for example, which of the living things in the aquaria need water. Then draw an arrow from water to each of the living things to indicate the dependent relationship. Use this single arrow to indicate any other dependent relationships.

■ When you get to the snail/elodea relationship, draw arrows in both directions to indicate that each gets something from the other. Use this double arrow to indicate any other interdependent relationships as well. Use a question mark to indicate a relationship the class is not sure about. See Figure 5-3 for an example of a completed web.

Figure 5-3

Example of completed aquarium web

- Ask the students to look at all of the relationships that are marked with a double arrow. Let them know that these are considered **interdependent relationships.** Ask students what they think interdependence means.

- Now cross out or erase just one of the circled items (for example, snail). Ask the students to name those things in the ecosystem affected by the loss of the snail. Use this example to demonstrate the importance of interdependent relationships.

Note: Save the web for use in Lesson 7. Remember to rewrite the word you chose to erase on the web. You may want to leave the web on display and add to it as students observe new relationships.

Final Activities

1. Remind students that they need to continue to make and record observations in the aquaria and terraria, noting the date each time. These daily observations will help them establish what the normal patterns are in the ecosystems. Ask students to predict some changes they might watch for in the coming weeks. They may mention growth, birth, death, and the accumulation of waste matter.

2. Ask students to write a paragraph or two in their science notebooks on this question: What would happen to your ecosystem if all the plants in it died? Encourage them to illustrate their explanations.

3. In the next lesson, students will add animals to their terraria. Ask students to predict how the crickets and isopods may affect the plant life. Also ask them to predict any changes that might occur in the terraria.

4. Now that the students have had at least one week to observe the changes in plant growth within their terraria, assign the reading selection on pg. 31 of the Student Activity Book (pg. 82 of this guide). Having observed germination firsthand, they should have a good grasp on the content here. Students should be prepared to discuss what they have read and observed on plant growth.

Extensions

`SCIENCE`

1. Hold a brainstorming session about other aquatic ecosystems, both salt water and fresh water. Have students list as many ecosystems as they can and web the dependent and interdependent relationships.

`ART` `LANGUAGE ARTS`

2. Encourage students to read about other aquatic ecosystems. Then use the collected class information to create a mural of a chosen aquatic ecosystem.

`SCIENCE`

3. Challenge students to research the role of bacteria in aquatic ecosystems.

Reading Selection

Growing Plants: How Seeds Spring to Life

Isn't nature amazing? Just give a seed water and the right temperature and watch it spring into new life.

Moisture is very important to sprouting, or **germination.** In your own terrarium, for instance, never allow seeds to dry out once you have planted them. Be sure to check your terrarium daily. Sprinkle it gently when the top of the soil surface seems dry.

Temperature is important, too. Most seeds will germinate at 22°C to 25°C (72°F to 78°F). This is a comfortable temperature for most people, too. So if you are comfortable, then probably all is well with your seeds.

It's interesting that most kinds of seeds do not need light to germinate. (That makes sense since they are under ground.) But once a plant sprouts from the seed, it needs lots of light to produce its own food.

Inside of bean

Seed coat

Leaves

Embryo (baby plant)

Cotyledon (food supply)

Radicle (embryonic root)

Tiny Food Warehouse

So what happens before a plant gets into the light and can start making food? Each seed carries along its own built-in warehouse of food. This gives it enough energy to start growing. Look at the picture of the inside of a bean seed.

Only a small part of the seed is the baby plant, or **embryo.** The rest is all stored food.

In nature, not every seed germinates. Can you think of some reasons why? Well, some are eaten, some rot, and some fall into places where they can't grow (rivers or paved walkways, for instance). That is why most plants produce so many seeds—to make sure that life continues, no matter what.

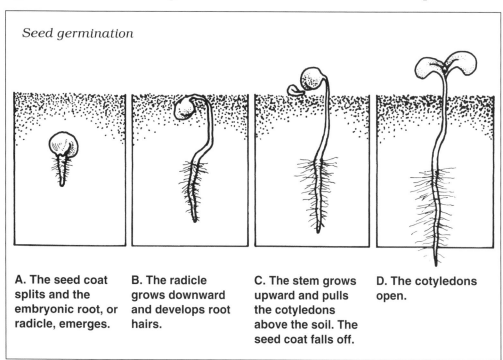

Seed germination

A. The seed coat splits and the embryonic root, or radicle, emerges.

B. The radicle grows downward and develops root hairs.

C. The stem grows upward and pulls the cotyledons above the soil. The seed coat falls off.

D. The cotyledons open.

LESSON 6

Adding Animals to the Terrarium

Overview and Objectives

Following the pattern of Lessons 4 and 5 in which students built a stable aquatic ecosystem, students now add animals to their terraria to complete a stable land ecosystem. Through discussion, students verify the predictions they made about plant growth in Lesson 2 and reinforce their understanding of plants as producers. As they record initial observations of the terrarium animals, students analyze the role organisms play in a stable ecosystem. This analysis prepares students to make further predictions about how living things affect each other.

- Students continue to observe and record plant growth in the terraria.

- Students make observations and record descriptions of the animals they add to their terraria.

- Students identify and record similarities and differences between crickets and isopods.

- Students continue to discuss their concepts of the word "ecosystem."

- Through reading selections, students learn more about crickets and isopods.

Background

Although this lesson focuses on terrestrial animals, it also reinforces the important role of plants in an ecosystem. Without plants, the animals students put into the terrarium today would not survive.

The reading selections in this lesson offer important background information on the isopods and crickets that students will now add to their terraria. Remember to assign these selections only after students have observed the animals firsthand.

Isopods are relatively slow moving and easy to handle, but the lively crickets present a challenge. Like all insects, their level of activity decreases with a drop in temperature. To slow them down temporarily, simply cool them in a refrigerator (not the freezer) for 20 minutes or so before you begin the lesson. Brief refrigeration causes no harm and greatly simplifies distribution. (See Appendix A for more information on receiving and maintaining the animals.)

The students will not be adding animals to the seven class terraria, which will be used in the pollution experiments in Lessons 11 and on.

Materials

For each student

1   science notebook
1   **Record Sheet 6-A: Adding Crickets and Isopods**

For every two students

1   terrarium planted in Lesson 2
1   cut-off bottle base with holes in it for a terrarium lid
1   hand lens
2   crickets
2   isopods
2   clear plastic cups
2   index cards for covering cups
2   spoons

For the teacher

1   knife

Preparation

1.   Put three holes in each terrarium lid, if you haven't already.

2.   Duplicate **Record Sheet 6-A.**

3.   Set out the crickets and isopods in their holding containers and place them in the distribution center. If you have access to a refrigerator, first chill the crickets for 20 to 30 minutes to slow them down. You may want to conceal the animals until distribution.

Procedure

1.   Ask students to pick up the terraria and hand lenses and place them nearby. Encourage students to use the hand lenses to observe the terraria during the discussion. Continue to encourage students to verify or challenge other classmates' observations by looking for evidence in their own terraria.

2.   Give students time to make and record observations with their teammates and to review notes in their science notebooks. Ask the students to look over and share their notebook predictions from Lesson 2 regarding the seeds in the terraria. Encourage them to compare growth of their own terraria (and the class terraria) with their predictions.

3.   Invite students to share their observations and what they have learned by reading about seed germination. The following questions will help guide the discussion:

   ■   How long did it take for the seeds to germinate? How many germinated?

   ■   Can you observe any roots? Compare the different plants' roots.

   ■   What happened to the seed coats on your seeds? What is the job of seed coats?

   ■   Do you remember why we call plants producers? Why did we wait until now to add the animals?

   ■   Compare these plants with the ones we put into the aquaria. Create a Venn diagram to help students visualize this comparison (see Figure 6-1).

Figure 6-1

Sample Venn diagram

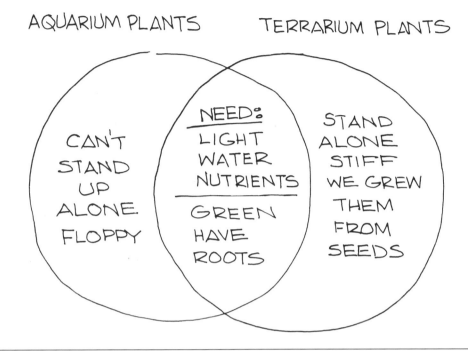

VENN DIAGRAM

AQUARIUM PLANTS   TERRARIUM PLANTS

CAN'T STAND UP ALONE. FLOPPY

NEED:
LIGHT
WATER
NUTRIENTS

GREEN
HAVE
ROOTS

STAND ALONE STIFF WE GREW THEM FROM SEEDS

4. Have students share their notebook entries from Step 2 of the previous lesson's **Final Activities.** Ask them to predict what would happen to their terraria if all the plants in the terraria died. Ask students to record these predictions in their notebooks.

5. Go over the instructions on pgs. 90–91 on how to add isopods and crickets to the terrarium (also on pgs. 36–37 of the Student Activity Book).

6. Distribute **Record Sheet 6-A: Adding Crickets and Isopods,** or use it as a model.

7. Point out the holding containers of isopods and crickets in the distribution center. Emphasize that students must use a gentle touch. Have students use the instructions on pgs. 36–37 when they get their materials from the distribution center.

8. Let student teams add the animals to their terraria. As you circulate, make sure they are handling the animals appropriately. Remind students to observe the animals with their hand lenses and to record observations.

9. As students complete their work, have them place the terraria back in the designated location and return supplies to the distribution center.

Final Activities

1. Invite students to share their initial observations of isopods and crickets with the class.

   ■ How are your two crickets alike? How are they different?

   ■ How are the crickets and isopods alike? How are they different?

   ■ What body parts did you notice?

   ■ What are some things that the animals did?

2. Have students compare the land and water ecosystems. Ask them if their definition of "ecosystem" has changed at all since observing two different ecosystems firsthand.

3. Remind students that they are responsible for making and recording daily observations on both the aquatic and the terrestrial ecosystems (and on the class ecosystems). If possible, designate a time for this each day. Remind them to keep looking for interdependent relationships within their own ecosystems.

4. Assign the reading selections on isopods and crickets starting on pg. 38 of the Student Activity Book (pg. 92 of this guide).

Extensions

SOCIAL STUDIES

1. Many cricket behaviors are similar to human behaviors: touching, cleaning, hiding, and fighting. Have students compare cricket behavior to human behavior.

MATHEMATICS

2. Find out if the house crickets used in this unit really can tell temperature. Ask student teams to figure out the room temperature in Celsius and Fahrenheit, using the following formulas:

   ■ To find the temperature using the Celsius scale, count the number of a cricket's chirps for 60 seconds, subtract 4, divide that number by 7.2, and then add 10. The total should be the same as the room temperature.

   $C = (n-4)/7.2 + 10$

   ■ To find the temperature using the Fahrenheit scale, count the number of a cricket's chirps for 60 seconds, subtract 4, divide that number by 4, and then add 50. The total should be the same as the room temperature.

   $F = (n-4)/4 + 50$

MATHEMATICS

3. Field crickets have a different chirping rate from that of the house crickets. See if your students can find out the formula for field crickets. Catch some field crickets and test them out.

SCIENCE

4. Students may enjoying trapping some "wild" isopods outside. Slice a large potato in half and hollow out each half. Secure the two halves together with string, rubber bands, or toothpicks. Cut a bit off one end of the potato to make an opening for the isopods to enter the trap. Place the trap where it is cool and damp and there is some leaf matter. Cover it with a little soil and some dead leaves. Check the trap every few days to see if any isopods have entered to feed on the inside of the potato.

SCIENCE   **LANGUAGE ARTS**

5. Challenge students to find out how isopods differ from insects.

SCIENCE

6. Supply your students with microscopes and droppers so they can observe microscopic organisms in their aquarium water. Have students put a drop or two of aquarium water on a slide, place a cover slip over the droplets, and place it under the microscope. Ask students to draw their findings. Also have them research the term "microorganisms" and identify what type of microorganisms they have found. Students can repeat this activity in later lessons. Ask them to predict how the number and type of microorganisms may change as the aquarium sits.

SCIENCE

7. Have students find pond, lake, or other water in a natural environment. Place the water in a cup with some green blades of grass. After the cup sits in a lit area for several days, have students observe the water under a microscope. What microorganisms do they see? How are the microorganisms the same as or different from the ones in the aquarium water?

Assessment

1. By now students should have developed some "animal sense"; that is, they should know how to handle living creatures appropriately. You can evaluate this skill as you observe them placing the crickets and isopods into their terraria during this lesson and when they handle these organisms throughout the unit.

2. Compare the drawings in this lesson with those from earlier lessons. Are there any differences in detail? Have students labeled parts correctly?

Management Tips

■ Remind students to schedule "rainfalls" in their terraria (and the seven class terraria) whenever the surface of the soil appears dry. Have them record the number of drops of water that their terraria (and the seven class terraria) will handle each time.

■ If crickets are rapidly devouring their food supply, let students add more seeds to the terrarium. Remind students to use their toothpicks to plant the seeds slightly below the soil level. This might help deter the crickets from eating the seeds.

Student Instructions for Adding Isopods to the Terrarium

1. Use a spoon to scoop two isopods into your clear plastic cup.

2. Return to your seat and observe your isopods closely with the hand lens. Record your observations. Include information on size, color, movement, and body parts. Illustrate and label your observations.

3. Place your isopods gently in the terrarium and watch what they do for two or three minutes. Record your observations.

Student Instructions for Adding Crickets to the Terrarium

1. Capture two crickets. There are lots of different ways to do it. Be sure you are very gentle.

   - If they are cold and slow-moving, you may be able to scoop them up easily with your cup and spoon.

   - Shake one or two off the egg carton, twig, or paper towel in the holding container into your cup.

   - Clamp your upside-down cup over the cricket, slip an index card underneath the cup, and turn the cup over with the cricket inside.

2. Cover the cup with the index card and return to your seat to observe the cricket with the hand lens. Record your observations. Include information on size, color, movement, and body parts. Illustrate and label your observations.

3. Gently place your crickets in the terrarium and watch what they do for two or three minutes. Record your observations.

4. Make certain that the cut-off base of your terrarium, which will be used for the terrarium lid, has three or four holes in it. If it does not, ask your teacher to make these holes with a knife.

5. Cover the terrarium with this lid to keep the crickets from hopping out.

Reading Selection

Isopods: More Like a Lobster!

Scientists call them isopods, which means "equal legs." But you probably know them by some other names, like wood louse, pill bug, sow bug, or roly-poly. Isopods are not insects. In fact, they are close relatives of lobsters, crabs, and shrimp. Like those sea creatures, most isopods live in water. There are a few land-living, or **terrestrial,** kinds of isopods, though. Yours belong to this group.

Look at your isopod with a hand lens. You will see a flat oval body covered by smooth, hard plates. It seems to be covered in a suit of armor. That stiff suit of armor is actually a skeleton. But unlike our skeleton, it's worn on the outside and is called an **exoskeleton.** At the head end is a pair of antennae and two tiny eyes.

Now, count the pairs of legs. If your isopod has six pairs of legs, it is very young and has not experienced its first **molt.** What is a molt? The isopod's exoskeleton is good protection, but it cannot grow. So in order to grow, the isopod must shed its old exoskeleton, or "molt." After the molt, it will have seven pairs of legs.

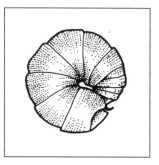

Pill bugs curl up into a ball to protect themselves.

Half a Molt Is Better than None

It's odd: the isopod sheds only half of its exoskeleton at a time. Usually the front half goes first. Check your isopod's color. Is the color all dark gray or black? Then the isopod has been wearing this exoskeleton for some time. Is the color light gray, or maybe even half light and half dark? Then the isopod has just experienced a molt. Or, it is in mid-molt.

The isopod breathes through specialized organs similar to fish gills. So, like its water-living, or **aquatic,** relatives, the isopod needs moisture at all times. (Keep this in mind whenever you schedule a rain shower for your terrarium. Wet the isopods' corner, too.)

The isopod has many predators, mostly birds, lizards, and spiders. (That is why some isopods, the pill bugs, curl up into a ball to protect themselves.) But isopods are more than just food for other animals. Isopods are **scavengers.** They eat dead and decaying plant matter. What animal in your aquarium also does this job?

Be on the lookout for baby isopods. If you are lucky enough to have a pregnant female, she may be bulging with up to 200 eggs in her brood pouch! How many legs will each baby have? How do you imagine they will look?

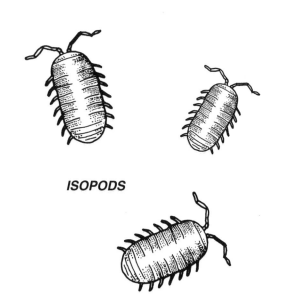

ISOPODS

Reading Selection

Crickets: A Closer Look

You probably recognize the cheerful chirping of crickets at night. But have you ever looked at a cricket up close? Crickets are insects. An insect's body is divided into three main parts: the head, the midsection (or **thorax**), and the abdomen. Look at your own crickets to identify these parts.

You have a **house cricket** in your terrarium. Attached to the house cricket's head are the eyes, the chewing mouth parts, and the antennae. (Use your hand lens to get a closeup look.) The antennae are almost as long as the cricket's whole body. They tell the insect about the feel, taste, smell, humidity, and temperature of the world outside.

Attached to the cricket's thorax you will find four wings. These will give you clues about your cricket's age. A very young cricket, or **nymph,** has no wings at all. A larger adolescent (teenage) cricket has very short wings. And the largest crickets, the adults, have full-grown wings.

Although the house cricket's wings are weak, they do have a purpose: chirping. But only the adult males can chirp. The sound comes from scraping one wing against another. Why do you think male crickets chirp?

Mighty Jumpers
Also attached to the thorax are the cricket's mighty legs. Count them. Notice that each pair is different. Which are the most powerful? Crickets can jump about 60 cm (2 ft). Let's compare that with how far a person could jump if he or she had the cricket's strength. A 180-cm (6-foot) tall person who had the same ability as a cricket would be able to jump 4,320 cm (144 ft)!

On the back section, or **abdomen,** look for more clues to your cricket's identity. Both males and females have two spines called **cerci** projecting out of the rear of the abdomen. Crickets use these to sense vibrations in the air and ground. But only the adult female has a third projection: a longer, dark, needlelike projection, or **ovipositor.** She uses it to place her eggs in the ground.

FEMALE CRICKET

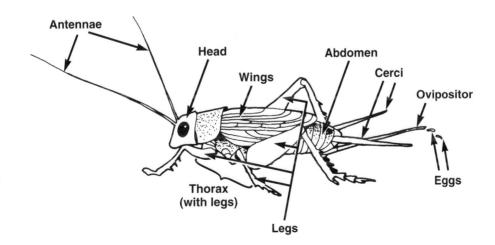

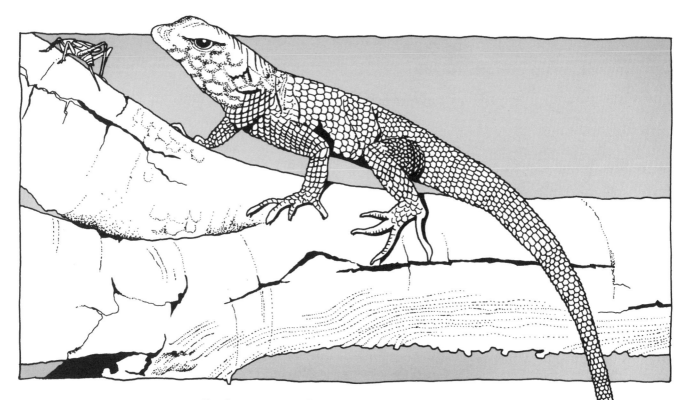

Crickets are a valuable part of the food chain.

The eggs are very small, banana shaped, and yellowish white. They usually hatch in two to three weeks. But the newly hatched babies (or nymphs) are so tiny that it is hard to see them without a hand lens. In four to eight weeks, after several molts, they are mature adults.

Crickets are food for such animals as birds, snakes, lizards, frogs, and toads. They are a valuable part of the food chain. But they also eat plants and can do a lot of damage to them. In some places, farmers consider them pests.

Just by observing your crickets, you can learn a lot. In fact, you can find out how the cricket moves, eats, explores, defends its territory, mates, lays eggs, and hides. But how does a cricket hear with its legs? How does it breathe through holes in its body? To find the answers, do some research in the library or contact an expert in insects, an **entomologist.**

Record Sheet 6-A

Name: _____

Date: _____

Adding Crickets and Isopods

1. In the space below, draw one of your isopods. Label all the parts you can.

2. Now draw one of your crickets. Label all the parts you can.

Record Sheet 6-A   Name: _____

Adding Crickets and Isopods *(continued)*

3. Compare the cricket to the isopod. Fill in the table below to organize your observations.

Animal Observations Table

	Isopod	Cricket
Size		
Color		
Legs		
Wings		
Other Parts		
Motion		
What It Did		

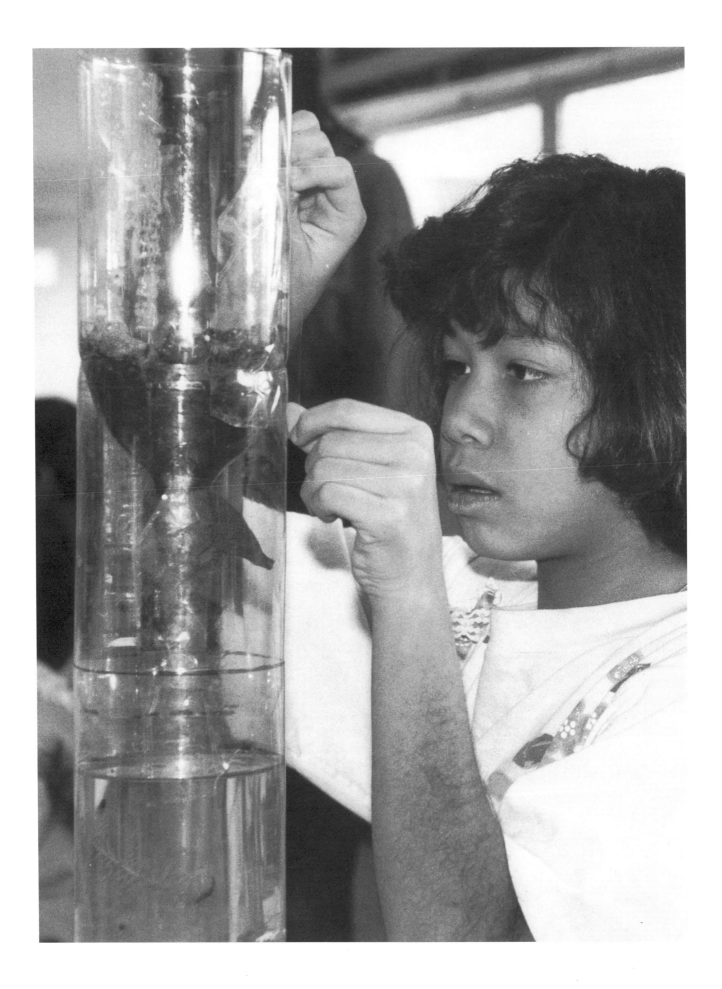

Joining the Terrarium and Aquarium

Overview and Objectives

After creating two ecosystems, students may have inferred that each member of an ecosystem has an important role in maintaining the ecosystem's stability. Using a terrestrial food chain wheel and a webbing activity, students learn more about the concepts of food chains, dependence, and interdependence. In this lesson, students compare land and aquatic ecosystems and reflect on how the two systems are interdependently related. Then, after physically joining their aquaria and terraria, students compare the resulting ecocolumn to earth's land and water systems.

- Using information from direct observations and reading, students discuss their terrestrial and aquatic ecosystems.

- Students explore food chains and consider the impact organisms have on one another.

- Students create a class web of their terrestrial ecosystem and compare it with Lesson 5's aquatic web.

- Students discuss the webs of both systems and compare them with the world's ecosystems.

- Students predict how one ecosystem might influence the other.

Background

Students may have found it a challenge to compare the two ecosystems for the first time in Lesson 6. Through a guided discussion and a webbing activity in this lesson, however, you can help them organize their thoughts and make valid comparisons.

Some of these comparisons are obvious. Plants in both systems are green and need light, air, nutrients, and water. Algae, too, are green and need light, air, nutrients, and water. Animals need food, water, shelter, and oxygen. The animals' methods of locomotion also are easy for students to describe and compare.

Students may find it a little more difficult to compare what each organism gives to and takes from its ecosystem. In ecosystems, plants and algae are **producers.** They also provide shelter, protection, and oxygen to the system, although the oxygen exchange is not an observable contribution.

To help the class compare the two sets of animals, you may find it useful to define the animals' roles. For example, if students don't suggest it themselves, point out that snails and isopods are **scavengers** and clean up debris. Crickets and mosquito fish are **consumers.** All of the animals produce waste materials.

Even waste materials and dead organisms have a role. These are digested by microorganisms (decomposers), such as bacteria and fungi. The nutrients in these waste materials and dead organisms are then converted into chemicals that plants can take up through their root systems. The **Terrestrial Food Chain Wheel** touches upon part of the nutrient cycle and demonstrates the concepts of dependence and interdependence.

After students join their two ecosystems into one ecocolumn (and create the seven class ecocolumns), you will ask them to speculate on how the land and water ecosystems might affect one another. At this point, students may offer dramatic examples from the real world, such as the destruction of a terrestrial environment by a tidal wave. Events in their ecocolumns will be on a much smaller scale, of course, but for now accept all ideas.

Materials

For each student

- 1 science notebook
- 1 copy of the **Terrestrial Food Chain Wheel** (blackline master on pg. 105)

For every two students

- 1 terrarium
- 1 aquarium
- 1 connector, bottle part C
- 4 strips of sealing tape
- 1 hand lens

Note: Use these same materials for each of the seven class ecocolumns.

For the class

- 1 overhead transparency of the **Terrestrial Food Chain Wheel**
  Overhead projector
  Scissors
  Web of aquatic relationships (from Lesson 5)
- 2 sheets of newsprint
  Markers

Preparation

1. Cut four 10-cm (4-in) pieces of tape for each pair of students and for each class ecocolumn.

2. Set out the materials in the distribution center.

3. Display the class's web of aquatic relationships from Lesson 5.

4. Duplicate the blackline master **Terrestrial Food Chain Wheel** (pg. 105) onto sturdy paper so that it is rigid (65-lb paper works well). Make one copy for each student.

5. Create an overhead transparency of the Terrestrial Food Chain Wheel. Cut off the guide. You will not need it.

6. Set up the overhead projector.

7. Set out the class terraria and aquaria.

8. This is a long lesson. Decide if you want to divide it into two parts. A possible dividing point is indicated on pg. 102.

Procedure

1. Have students pick up the three separate components of their ecocolumns: the terrarium, the aquarium, and the connector.

2. Give students a few minutes to review previous notes, observe their two ecosystems and the class ones, and record observations. Then invite them to share observations and what they have learned about their terraria through reading.

3. Distribute a copy of the **Terrestrial Food Chain Wheel** to each student and discuss the directions.

4. Give the students time to cut and tape together the Terrestrial Food Chain Wheel and its sliding guide. Remind them to cut carefully and remove the wheel's inner circle. Inaccurate cutting may skew the wheel's readings.

5. Now let students sit with their partners and experiment with moving the guide around the circular model, discussing any relationships they see on the model.

6. Review the difference between dependent and interdependent relationships.

7. Use the overhead transparency of the Terrestrial Food Chain Wheel to guide a discussion on food chains. Ask questions such as the following:

   ■ What are the dependent relationships on the wheel?

   ■ What are the interdependent relationships on the wheel?

8. Now ask students to use their sliding guides to find out what would happen within the terrarium if the crickets were destroyed. Use this question for each relationship in the terrarium.

   Note: Make certain the students keep these wheels. They will be reused in Lesson 12.

9. Have students look at the web of aquatic relationships from Lesson 5. Ask them to summarize the process they went through to develop it and to describe the difference between an arrow drawn in one direction (represents a dependent relationship) and one drawn in both directions (represents an interdependent relationship).

10. Invite students to develop a similar web for the terrarium.

    ■ First, give students three or four minutes to discuss the terrarium web with their partners.

    ■ Then have them each draw a quick sketch of this web in their science notebooks.

    ■ As a class, discuss and then construct the new web. Systematically work through each element (both living and nonliving) until everything in the terrestrial ecosystem has been included in some way in the web. Figure 7-1 shows a sample class web. Yours may be different.

11. Hang the class's aquatic and terrestrial webs side by side. Ask students to look for similarities in the two ecosystems. Ask them to select a "pair to compare." Begin with the plants.

    ■ How are the plants in the two systems alike?

    ■ What do they need to live?

    ■ What do they give to their ecosystem?

Figure 7-1

Sample web of terrestrial relationships

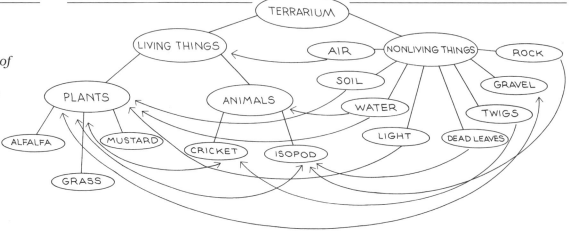

Compare two of the animals, one from each ecosystem.

■ Do they need the same things to live?

■ What do they give to their ecosystem?

Management Tip: If you decide to divide this lesson into two parts, this is one logical place to stop.

12. In the real world, ecosystems do not exist alone. They all touch one another in some way. So, too, will your ecosystems touch each other. Explain that now students will put their ecosystems together into a three-part stack called an "ecocolumn."

13. Go over the instructions at the end of this lesson (pg. 44 of the Student Activity Book) and have students build their ecocolumns.

Note: Remind volunteers to complete the seven class ecocolumns. Place them in a naturally lit area so that the aquarium plants and algae thrive. If you find it necessary, periodically have the volunteers separate the aquaria from the terraria and use a pipette to facilitate the exchange of gases.

Final Activities

1. Look at the two webs again. Ask students to speculate on how the two entire ecosystems (terrarium and aquarium) might relate to each other. How could something that happens in the terrarium affect the aquarium? If no one has an idea, remind students that they removed the bottle cap from the terrarium so the extra liquid in the terrarium would run off into the aquarium.

2. Ask students to think of an example in the real world where a land ecosystem influences a water ecosystem or vice versa. If students find this question a challenge, let them know that often a natural disaster in one ecosystem (such as a flooded river) could affect another ecosystem (such as the land and habitats around the river).

3. Have students observe their own ecocolumns. Ask them to write a paragraph or two in their science notebooks predicting how a change in their terraria might cause a change in their aquaria.

4. Have students put their completed ecocolumns and the class ecocolumns in the designated place and return all materials to the distribution center.

Management Tip: Remind students to make and record daily observations on their own ecocolumns and the seven class ones.

Extensions

| LANGUAGE ARTS | | SOCIAL STUDIES |

1. Suggest that students write about a natural disaster and how it could affect an ecosystem that they know well. The topic could be, for example, What would happen if a bolt of lightning knocked down the tree in my back yard?

| SCIENCE |

2. There are a number of commercial card games and board games on ecosystems. Have students create their own ecosystem card or board games.

| SOCIAL STUDIES | | LANGUAGE ARTS |

3. Ask students to bring in and discuss examples from magazines or newspapers of both natural and human-made ecological disasters.

Assessment

1. In the next three lessons, note the quality of students' observations in both discussion and writing. They should be showing improvement in accuracy, detail, and clarity. Watch, too, for use of new vocabulary. Figure 7-2 provides a short checklist to help you assess students' progress.

2. Use each student's notebook entry from the **Final Activities** as an embedded assessment. It will give you an idea of how well each student can conceptualize the idea of interdependence between the two ecosystems.

   ■ Did the student list a specific and realistic change to the terraria (for example, adding contaminated water to the terraria would cause a reduction in the number of duckweed and algae)?

   ■ Did the student give reasons why this change might affect the aquaria?

Figure 7-2

Assessment Checklist

Observations

❑ Accurate

❑ Detailed

❑ Clear

❑ Complete

Discussions

❑ Discusses dependent relationships

❑ Discusses interdependent relationships

❑ Compares plant pairs

❑ Compares animal pairs

Student Instructions for Putting the Ecocolumn Together

1. Remove the bottle cap from the base of the terrarium. Leave it off for the rest of the unit.

2. Pick up four strips of tape.

3. Stack your bottles as pictured.

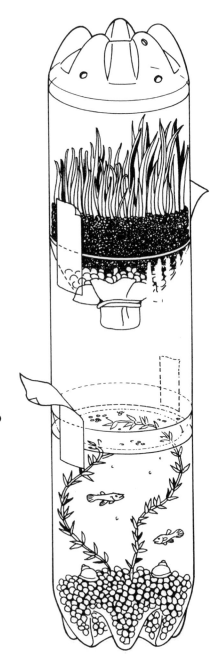

4. Use two pieces of tape to attach part A (the aquarium) to part C (the connector). Use two pieces of tape to hold part T (the terrarium) to part C.

   Helpful hint: Turn under one corner of each piece of tape to make it easier to get the tape off later.

Terrestrial Food Chain Wheel

Directions: Cut out the circular food chain wheel and the sliding guide. Make certain you cut out the center of the model. Fold the flaps of the guide around the model. Tape the two flaps together so that the guide slides easily.

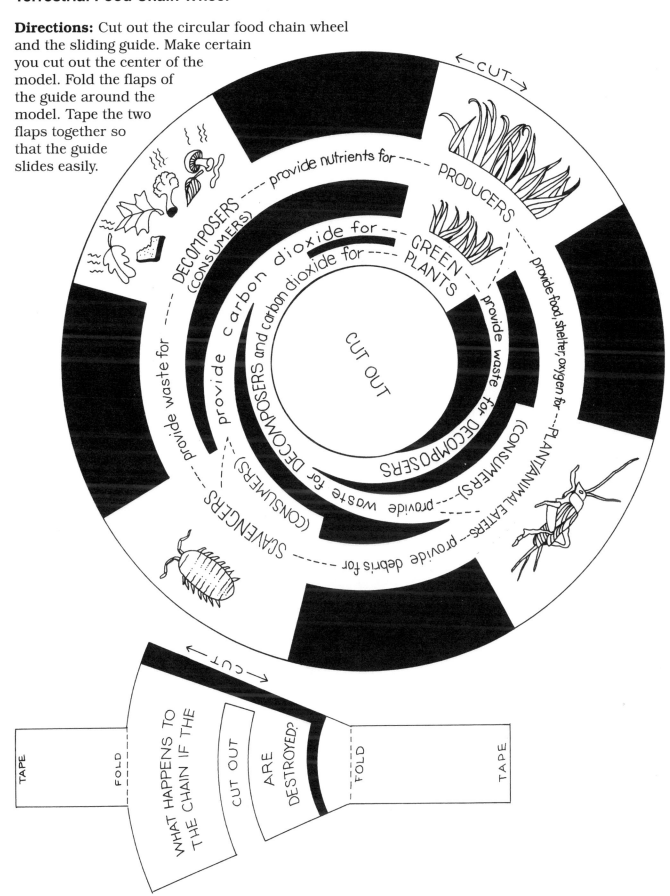

Upsetting the Stability

Overview and Objectives

Using their two model ecosystems as examples, students in this lesson are introduced to the concept of "stable" and "disturbed" ecosystems. After identifying systems that have become disrupted through natural causes, students read about disturbances caused by human activity. Identifying human-made pollutants and analyzing which of these pollutants can be used in a classroom pollution experiment sets the stage for students to plan their own pollution experiments in Lesson 10.

- Students observe, describe, and compare stable and disturbed ecocolumns.

- Students become familiar with pH paper.

- Students identify and discuss some natural causes that can disturb an ecosystem.

- Students read and write about human-made disturbing forces, or pollutants.

- Students reflect on their own learning through a self-assessment.

Background

The students' ecocolumns probably are flourishing right now, providing examples of stable ecosystems. The plants and algae should be producing enough food for all inhabitants. The water should be clear and odorless, the soil dark brown, and the animals thriving.

But natural events may have occurred to disturb a system or two, and you can take advantage of these to lead into today's discussion. For example, if multiple births have occurred in a system, the food supply may be running low. If a death has occurred (particularly in the water) the build-up of bacteria may cause a foul smell and discoloration.

As in the students' ecocolumns, disturbing forces occur naturally in the larger world. In nature, ecosystems change in response to these forces in an unending process.

Unfortunately, most disturbing forces today are human-made. One type is a **pollutant;** that is, anything that can harm living organisms when too much of it is released into the ecosystem. Pesticides, fertilizers, nuclear waste, garbage, and exhaust fumes are all pollutants that can upset the stability of ecosystems on land, in the air, and in the water. **Pollution** is the condition that results when pollutants interact with the environment.

Figure 8-1

Natural disasters

The reading selections in this lesson will give students background information about three common pollutants: acid rain, road salt, and fertilizer. In this lesson, you will divide your class into six groups and assign one pollutant and its accompanying reading selection to every two groups. Students in each group will be asked to read about only one pollutant to prepare for Lesson 9's presentation on that pollutant. They will learn about the other two pollutants from the other groups' presentations. Then, in Lesson 9, students will read about all three pollutants, since they will need this information for Lesson 11's pollution experiments and for Lesson 15 when they study the Chesapeake Bay.

One of the pollutants students will read about is acid rain. To help prepare for the reading selection on acid rain, students will now use pH paper to test for the presence or absence of acid. The pH scale was devised by a Danish biochemist, Soren Sorensen, in 1909. The pH is the value of a solution's **acidity** or **basicity** (or **alkalinity**) in terms of the relative amounts of hydrogen ions (H+) and hydroxide ions (OH-). The initials "pH" represent two French words, *pouvoir hydrogene,* which mean "hydrogen power."

The pH scale's values range from 0 to 14. **Acidic** solutions have pH values below 7, with the most acidic solutions having a pH value near 0. **Basic,** or **alkaline,** solutions have pH values above 7, with the most basic solutions having a pH value near 14. The pH of a **neutral** solution—a solution that is neither acidic nor basic—is 7. To test the pH of vinegar in this lesson, and of the ecocolumns in Lesson 11, students will use an indicator—pH paper—that changes color as the pH changes. This pH paper has a color range from yellow (most acidic) to green (least acidic). Testing vinegar for pH shows students what happens to the paper in the presence of extreme acidity and prepares them for analyzing acidity results when they test the ecocolumns in Lessons 11 and 12.

Note: Although we often refer to acid rain as a pollutant, it is, strictly speaking, a by-product of two pollutants: sulfur dioxide and nitrogen oxide. You may want to review the reading selections at the end of this unit now and clarify these points with your students.

Materials

For each student
- 1   science notebook
- 1   copy of **Student Self-Assessment** (blackline master on pgs. 198–199)
- 2   strips of pH paper

For every two students
- 1   ecocolumn
- 1   dropper

For the class
- Vinegar
- Water
- 15   cups, 30 ml (1 oz)
- 2   droppers
- 1   sheet of newsprint or transparency film
- Markers

Preparation

1. Scan the ecocolumns to identify any that have become disturbed naturally.

2. Try to add supplemental materials to the learning center to provide more information on pollution problems.

3. Obtain materials to record student ideas. Title the sheet "Pollution Caused by Humans."

4. Plan how you will divide your class into six groups—two per pollutant. Keep student pairs together in each group, since they will be using their own ecocolumns (with animals) in upcoming lessons as well.

5. Cut the pH paper into 5-cm (2-in) strips.

6. Make a copy of the **Student Self-Assessment** (blackline master on pgs. 198–199) for each student.

Procedure

1. Invite the class to share notebook entries from Lesson 7. Ask students if they have any new ideas about how one of their ecosystems might affect the other.

2. Encourage students to talk about those ecosystems that have become naturally disturbed in some way (for example, births, deaths, plants that died or were eaten). Challenge them to explain what happened and what the consequences to the ecosystem were.

   Note: If no births or deaths have occurred, ask students to imagine the situation and its consequences.

3. Discuss other natural disruptive forces on earth (for example, volcanoes, earthquakes, lightning, and fire). If any students did Extension 1 from Lesson 7, let them share their ideas on how a natural disaster can affect an ecosystem they know well.

4. Explain that natural disasters account for only a part of ecological disruption. Unfortunately, humans are responsible for the rest: we release pollutants into the environment. State that one definition of **pollutant** is "anything that can harm living organisms when too much of it is released into an ecosystem." Ask students to jot in their science notebooks a quick list of the ways humans pollute. Help the students understand that the term "pollution" is the condition that results when pollutants interact with the environment.

5. Show students the sheet you have prepared, "Pollution Made by Humans." Ask them to share their lists with the class. Record all ideas. When students offer duplicate ideas, put a check next to the first one to acknowledge all contributions.

6. Now review the class list and ask students to speculate on which of the ways humans pollute could be duplicated in a class ecosystem to study. Explain that any pollutant used in the study must fulfill two criteria:

   - It has to be fairly common and easily obtainable.
   - It cannot be toxic to people in small doses.

7. Ask students how vinegar, fertilizer, and salt could be used to simulate three common pollutants.

8. Let students know that vinegar is similar to one pollutant, acid rain, in that both are acidic. Distribute two strips of pH paper to each student. Distribute two 30-ml cups to each group of four students. Use one dropper to put a few drops of water in one of the cups. Then use a second dropper to place a few drops of vinegar in the second cup. Let students determine what happens when the pH paper is dipped in each liquid.

9. Discuss results. Which liquid represents the pH of acid rain? Using the chart on the pH paper dispenser, discuss how the resulting colors represent different levels of acidity.

Final Activities

1. Divide your class into six groups. Let students know that each group will read about one of three common pollutants and will plan a presentation on that pollutant (see the reading selections beginning on pg. 48 of the Student Activity Book and pg. 112 of this guide).

2. Help the groups decide which one of the three pollutants they will read about. Be sure that two groups are assigned to each pollutant.

3. Let your students decide how they will make their presentations in Lesson 9. For example, an entire group can make a presentation to the class, or students can meet in teams of three, with one representative from each group.

4. Assign the appropriate reading selection to each group.

5. Give students time to read, take notes, and prepare for the presentations in Lesson 9.

6. Remind students to continue their daily observations and recordkeeping.

7. Explain to students that since they have worked through half of the unit, it is a good time to reflect on their own work. Distribute the **Student Self-Assessment.**

8. Have students complete the Self-Assessment and place it in their notebooks. Let students know that they will revisit this again at the end of the unit.

Management Tip: If the water becomes stagnant, you may find it necessary to have students use the dropper to aerate the aquaria periodically.

Extension

SOCIAL STUDIES

If possible, reserve a space on your bulletin board for current articles on pollution problems. Encourage students to contribute to it.

Assessment

If you review the **Student Self-Assessments** now, you will be able to judge whether a student views his or her work as adequate or whether a student is having difficulty working with a partner. You may want to discuss these issues with certain students and make any necessary changes or suggestions before Lesson 9.

Reading Selection

The Story behind Acid Rain

There is a lot of talk these days about acid rain. Do you know what acid rain is? Do you know if humans are involved in causing it?

The problem begins when we burn coal, oil, and gas, which are called **fossil fuels.** We burn these fuels in our cars, homes, or factories. Burning fuels release sulfur and nitrogen, which chemically combine with oxygen in the air. In this new combined form, the chemicals are known as **sulfur dioxide** and **nitrogen oxide.** Sulfur dioxide and nitrogen oxide are harmful to the environment and are called **pollutants.** (A pollutant is anything that can harm living organisms when too much of it is released into an ecosystem.) Both of those pollutants escape through

smokestacks, chimneys, and tailpipes and climb skyward as the fuel burns. Over 20 million tons of each of these two pollutants move into the atmosphere each year.

Sometimes these pollutants fall to the earth with dry particles, such as dust. Other times these pollutants become trapped by moisture in the clouds. When these pollutants chemically combine with water, they form new chemicals called **acids.** As you can see in the illustration, these acids (**sulfuric acid** and **nitric acid**) fall to earth in rain, snow, sleet, hail, or fog. This is polluted rain, called **acid rain** or **acid deposition.** Acid deposition can damage plants, animals, and buildings.

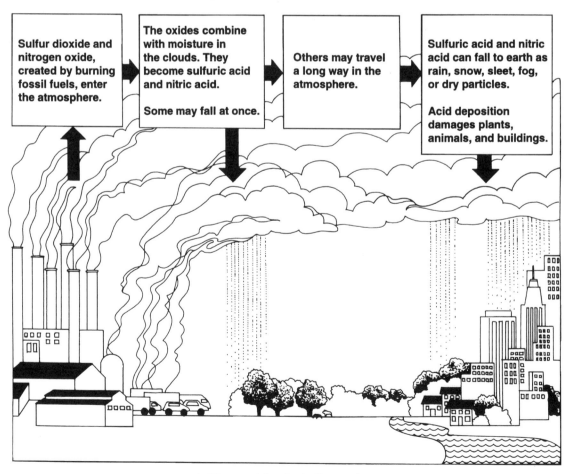

How acid rain is formed

How Do We Measure Acidity?

We can divide all chemicals into three categories: acid, base, or neutral. You already know some acids, such as vinegar and lemon juice. They have a sour, biting taste.

The chemical opposite of an acid is a **base.** Some bases you might know are baking soda, liquid bleach, and milk of magnesia (for acid indigestion!).

What happens when you mix an acid with a base? You make a **neutral** substance that is neither acid nor base. In other words, you have neutralized the acid with a base.

You already know there are degrees of temperature. Well, there are also degrees of acid and base. We use a special scale to measure acids and bases. It's called the **pH scale.**

The pH scale ranges from 0 (extremely acidic) to 14 (extremely basic). In between is 7, or neutral. Remember that the lower the number, the more acidic something is.

Use the pH scale below to answer these questions:

- Look at the pH scale and find pure distilled water. What is its pH? Is it an acid, base, or neutral?

- Locate the section labeled acid rain. What is the range of pH for acid rain? What are some other things that fall into the same range?

- Normal, uncontaminated rain is slightly acidic. Put your finger on the scale to show where normal rain might fall.

Why Are We Worried about Acid Rain?

A little acid in rain is normal. But a lot of acid rain disturbs many ecosystems, especially aquatic ones. For example, some kinds of animals are more sensitive to acid than others. While an adult wood frog can live in water with a pH level of 4, certain fish (like the rainbow trout and the smallmouth bass) cannot survive below pH 5.

pH SCALE

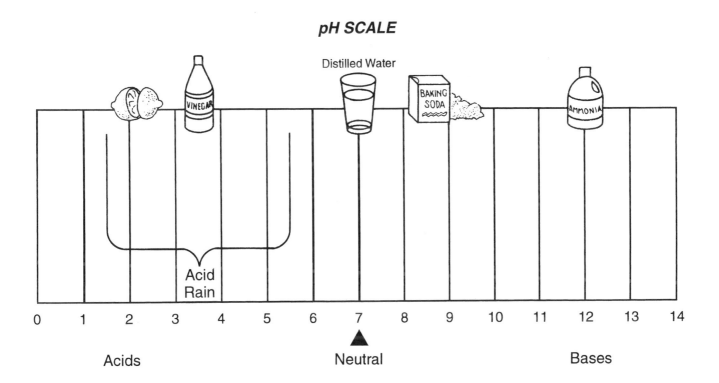

Clams, crayfish, snails, and mayflies are in trouble at pH 6. The eggs and larvae of aquatic creatures seem even more sensitive to low pH. Fewer eggs hatch, and fewer creatures grow to adults.

It's not easy for experts to measure acid rain's effects on terrestrial ecosystems. But it seems that too much acid in the soil may harm plants' root systems. Acid rain also seems to damage the leaves of sensitive trees.

Acid rain seems to change the soil, too. Acid releases certain chemicals (like aluminum) that normally stay locked up in the soil. These chemicals can poison some plants.

What Can We Do to Help?
Do you remember that when we burn fossil fuels, we generate the pollutants that form acid rain? The energy in fossil fuels heats, cools, and lights our homes. It also runs our vehicles, cooks our food, and runs our machinery. We aren't going to stop doing these things altogether. But we can each try to cut down. Every time we walk or bike instead of driving, or turn down the heat, or shut off extra lights, we help prevent pollution.

Reading Selection

Crops and Cows—What's the Problem?

Farming, or **agriculture,** produces the fruits, vegetables, and grains we need to survive. But the fertilizer used to grow these crops also pollutes our water systems. How can this be? Chemical fertilizers run off from fields. And animal manure runs off from barnyards and feedlots. Both are washed into ponds, streams, rivers, oceans, and even the water that runs underground.

Agricultural runoff

How Can a Fertilizer Pollute?

These **fertilizers** are rich in nutrients, especially nitrogen, phosphorus, and potassium. That's how they help crops grow. But if you think of a pollutant as anything that can harm living organisms when too much of it is released into the ecosystem, then fertilizers can be pollutants, too. Excess fertilizer can provide too many nutrients in a water system. So the body of water and the plants in it become too "well fed."

Overfed plants can grow so quickly that they choke waterways. When overfed, algae also reproduce rapidly. (This is called an **algae bloom,** which turns the water a bright green.) When the plants use up the nutrients in the water, they die and rot. When bacteria feed on this dead material, they use up valuable oxygen.

Manure is rich in nutrients, too. It also carries bacteria with it. In the water, these bacteria have a population explosion. This increase in bacteria takes away oxygen from the water. Sometimes, the bacteria use up so much oxygen that the plants and animals in the water suffocate and die.

What Can We Do?

We want to keep growing good crops. And many farmers need to keep raising cattle. So we will need to find solutions for the runoff problem. Many experts are researching ways to keep pollutants out of the water. They're trying to find out exactly how much fertilizer to spread on the soil for each type of crop. That way we won't use any more than we need. And the extra fertilizer won't wash into the water. Other scientists are experimenting with ways to recycle manure cheaply. What are your ideas?

Reading Selection

When Salt Isn't Safe

Have you ever ridden in a car in a snowstorm? Then you probably know that the roads can get awfully slippery. And that makes driving dangerous. In parts of the country where winters are fierce, the highway departments spread a mixture of sand and **road salt** on the roads. The sand helps tires get a grip. And the salt melts ice.

We want people who travel on these icy roads to be safe. But we are also concerned about the damage salt does. When spring comes and the snow and ice melt, salt dissolves in the water. Then passing cars wash or spray the salty water out to the roadside.

At the roadside, salt coats the bark of trees and soaks down into their roots. It "burns" the tops of tender new plants just coming out of the soil. Salt also covers plants that roadside animals such as rabbits and woodchucks depend on for food and shelter. It goes down through the soil to the water system below ground. Eventually, it runs into other bodies of water.

When salt enters a body of water such as a stream or a lake, it can cause harm there, too. Both plants and animals are sensitive to salt in different degrees. Take the egg and larval stages of many aquatic animals, for instance. Even the slightest increase in salt can kill them.

Is there a solution? We know that there are other chemicals that can melt ice just as well as salt does. However, these chemicals are more expensive. And while officials want the roads to be safe, they must consider costs when they make their decisions.

It's a Trade-off

Some areas have started using less harmful, but more expensive, chemicals. But many other areas are still dumping tons of salt on the roads every winter. If you were an official, what would you do?

Salt helps melt the ice and lets tires grip the road, but it can be harmful, too.

Reporting on Pollutants

Overview and Objectives

Building on the past eight lessons in which they created, observed, and analyzed model ecosystems, students now begin to shift their thoughts to a larger ecosystem—their own world. Through readings and classroom presentations about three common pollutants, students now learn how human-made pollutants can damage the environment. During the presentations, students gain experience in oral communication skills, reinforce listening skills, and practice leadership skills as they teach classmates about their assigned pollutant.

- Students make presentations about the three pollutants.
- Students discuss the trade-offs involved when humans release pollutants into the environment.
- Students record in their science notebooks important points and questions regarding each presentation.
- Students read about three pollutants.
- Students observe their ecosystems and record observations.

Background

In Lesson 8, you and your students should have decided how to make the group presentations in this lesson. Suggested presentation formats included the following:

- Each group gives a whole group presentation to the other five groups.
- Each group breaks into smaller teams, and the smaller teams each give a presentation on a specific item regarding their group's pollutant.
- Students meet in teams of three, with each member of that team representing a different pollutant. Each member of the team teaches the other two about his or her pollutant.

The two most important aspects of this lesson are students' acquiring information about all three pollutants and their interacting with one another during the presentations. Your role is mainly that of facilitator. Make sure that each group has enough time for its presentations and that any misleading information is clarified. Encourage a question-and-answer period at the end of each presentation.

Note: By now, some students may have inadvertently knocked over their ecocolumns. Students can rebuild the ecocolumns or join with another pair of students in their observations.

Materials

For each student
  1 science notebook

For each group
  Props (if applicable)
  Notes on their pollutant
  Chalkboard space

Preparation

1. Arrange the room to accommodate the presenters.

2. Obtain any audiovisual equipment students plan to use.

Procedure

1. Set the stage for the students' presentations by explaining that in Lesson 8 they each read about one pollutant that affects our environment. Let them know that in today's presentations they will learn about all three pollutants. Review the presentation format that the students decided upon in Lesson 8.

2. Review proper listening skills with your class. Explain that, as the audience, their role is just as important as the presenter's. Encourage your students to use their science notebooks during the presentations to record important points and questions they may have about each pollutant.

3. Proceed with the presentations and question and answer period. Encourage the students to research any incorrectly stated facts.

Final Activities

1. Explain that in the next class students will plan pollution experiments using the three pollutants they have just discussed.

2. Assign the two remaining reading selections so that each student has read about all three pollutants before Lesson 10.

3. Remind students to continue to record daily observations of their own (and the class) ecocolumns.

Management Tip: Remember that your class will need six empty 2-liter bottles to hold the pollutant solutions in Lesson 11.

SOCIAL STUDIES

Extension

Guest speakers can help to underscore the fact that pollutants cause problems in the real world. Here are some ideas for speakers:

■ A representative from a local industry to talk about what his or her company is doing to curb pollution

■ An agent from the state agricultural extension service or a farmer to talk about farming or landscaping practices in your area

■ An official from the highway department to talk about how roads are de-iced in your area (if this applies to where you live)

■ A naturalist, forest ranger, or environmental educator to talk about some of the effects pollutants have on the environment

■ An environmental lawyer to explain pollution control laws

Assessment

Determine your students' communication skills and baseline knowledge of the three pollutants by noting the following:

- Were students able to defend the ideas they presented?

- Were the facts clearly stated and precise?

- Were students' questions relevant to the content presented?

- Did students' notes accurately reflect the content of the presentation?

Planning Pollution Experiments

Overview and Objectives

In this lesson, students apply what they have learned about pollutants in Lessons 8 and 9. Following classroom discussions on acid rain, road salt, and fertilizer and on the trade-offs involved in using each one, students investigate those pollutants in a scientific experiment. In preparation for their pollution experiment, students use a planning worksheet to formulate a specific experimental question and make predictions about the results. Through this experience, students gain additional insight into the use of modeling to test and observe cause and effect.

- Students discuss and analyze the causes and effects of three types of pollution.

- Students plan experiments to study the effects of pollution.

- Students determine variables and controls and prepare to use simulations in a scientific investigation.

- Students predict the possible effects of pollutants on their model ecosystems.

- Students establish a recordkeeping system for their experiments.

Background

In this lesson, students observe the effects pollutants have on their model ecosystems, gaining a better understanding of how ecosystems thrive and suffer in the real world. Students also begin thinking about solutions to the environmental problems caused by these pollutants. Throughout the unit, your class has been maintaining seven class ecocolumns. Students now will witness pollution firsthand by actually polluting six of the class ecocolumns. Students will use the seventh one as a "control."

This lesson will run more smoothly if you have organized the class beforehand. Your first step is to regroup students into teams of four or five, with one class ecocolumn per team. A suggestion of how to organize and keep track of the teams is illustrated in Figure 10-1. Of course, you will have to adjust the illustration to suit the number of teams in your class.

Because students will be working in larger cooperative groups in the next lessons, take some time to discuss the importance of working together. Note that each member is expected to contribute to the group's work.

The class control ecocolumn serves an important function. Maintained in its natural, unpolluted state, it is the yardstick against which students will measure the pollutants' effects. The control serves as a reference point, an unchanged basis of comparison. Students also should use their own ecocolumns as a basis

Figure 10-1

How to organize teams

of comparison, although they are not true scientific controls (since they differ from the class ecocolumns in containing animals).

Students probably will have had little experience planning a scientific experiment. In a good experiment, all conditions are kept the same except one, known as the **experimental variable.** For example, all the class ecocolumns should get the same amount of light and water and be kept at about the same temperature. In addition, when watering the ecocolumns, students should use about the same number of dropperfuls of water that they have been using throughout the unit. This will prevent overwatering, which could skew the results caused by the pollutants. Only the condition students are testing should change.

Another way to explain the concept of altering only one variable is to call an experiment a "fair test." Children understand that for a track-and-field race to be a fair test of who is the fastest, all the runners must compete under the same conditions. They must all start from the same line, run on the same course, and end at the same finish line. Similarly, all the ecocolumns must "compete" under the same conditions.

Management Tip: This is a long lesson. Decide if you want to divide it into two parts. A possible stopping point is indicated on pg. 126.

Materials

For each student
  1 fact sheet (See **Preparation,** Step 3)

For each team of four students
  1 experimental class ecocolumn
  1 **Record Sheet 10-A: Planning Worksheet**
  1 fine-point permanent marker

For the class
  1 control ecocolumn
     pH paper

Preparation

1. Plan how you will regroup the class into no more than six teams with each team having four or five students (see Figure 10-1) and with one class ecocolumn per team. (Grouping will work best if you use the same teams as in Lesson 9.) Again, try to keep student pairs together in each team, since they will be testing the pH in their own ecocolumns (containing animals) in Lesson 11.

2. Assign a pollutant (either salt, vinegar, or fertilizer) to each team.

3. Duplicate the fact sheets on pgs. 128–130 (each student needs only one— the one matching his or her assigned pollutant).

4. Duplicate **Record Sheet 10-A: Planning Worksheet** (one for each team of four).

Procedure

1. Ask students what they learned about the three pollutants during Lesson 9's presentations. Use questions such as the following:

   ■ What causes each type of pollution? (Acid deposits from fossil fuels, overfertilization, and road salt.)

   ■ What are the effects of these kinds of pollutants?

   ■ Why do we continue to use fossil fuels, road salt, and fertilizers?

2. Group the students in no more than six teams of four or five students as you did in Lesson 9. Let each team select one class ecocolumn and label it with the names of the team members and the name of the pollutant they will test.

3. Introduce the experiment by using the race analogy. Ask the following questions:

   ■ When you run a race, what question are you trying to answer?

   ■ How do you set up the race to make it a fair test? What things must be kept the same for all runners?

4. Ask students how they could use the "fair test" idea to set up three experiments on pollution. Use the following questions to stress the importance of planning. Decide on some class rules ahead of time.

   ■ What question will your team try to answer?

   ■ What things will we have to keep the same for all six ecocolumns we will test?

5. Discuss the term "control." Then have a student volunteer label the seventh ecocolumn "Control." Ask students why this ecocolumn will not be polluted.

6. Discuss how students should use their own ecocolumns as a basis of comparison throughout the experiment. This process may help students see how an ecocolumn undisturbed by humans can thrive.

7. Distribute **Record Sheet 10-A: Planning Worksheet** and go over it with the class. Since this may be the first time students will set up an experiment on their own, go over each step carefully. For example:

   ■ In Step 1, students must decide on a specific amount of pollutant and how often they want to add it. Ask them to think of their previous experience watering the terraria. How many dropperfuls of water did they use to create a runoff into the aquaria?

   ■ Step 2 asks the students to formulate an experimental question. This question should be specific (for example, Will overfertilizing an ecosystem cause an overabundance of plant growth?).

   ■ In Step 3, students might include things such as light, temperature, and the number of drops of water as constants.

   ■ In Step 4, students should look for changes in the ecocolumn, such as color, size of plants, change in amount of algae, deaths, or odor.

8. Distribute the appropriate fact sheets to the teams. Give students time to read them over and ask questions before they begin planning their experiments.

9. Ask your students to think of the possible effects of overwatering. You may want to include the following questions in your discussion:

   ■ How many dropperfuls of water did you use throughout the unit to water your own ecocolumns?

   ■ How much water/pollutant solution should you use during each watering of the pollution experiments?

   ■ How often should you water (pollute) the terraria with the pollutant solution?

Management Tip: If you choose to divide this lesson into two parts, this is one place to stop.

10. Ask student teams to discuss Record Sheet 10-A and the fact sheets in their groups and come to an agreement on an experiment. Have them complete Record Sheet 10-A.

11. Collect the completed record sheets.

Final Activity

Challenge students to write in their notebooks several reasons why the control ecocolumn is important in the experiment.

Extensions

1. Take students outdoors to run a race. Let them make the rules. Afterwards, talk about whether it was a fair test.

   SCIENCE

2. Encourage students to investigate a pollutant other than the three discussed in this lesson. If the students want to implement an experiment using that pollutant, create an additional class ecocolumn that contains plants and algae only.

Assessment

In the next two lessons, review each team's plan for the pollution experiment (**Record Sheet 10-A**). Offer teams assistance as needed before they begin experimenting. Make certain that every team member understands his or her own group's decisions. Look for growth in the following areas:

- The plan is realistic and feasible.

- The plan details specific amounts of pollutant and frequency of application.

- The experimental question is narrow enough to be answered by the experiment itself. For example, What does salt do? is too broad. How does salt affect the plants in our ecocolumn? is better.

- Students have listed specific things to look for in their observations, such as changes in color, odor, or number of plants.

- Students give reasons for their predictions.

- Students list the conditions they will hold constant.

- Students establish and maintain an organized recordkeeping system for new data.

> **Note:** You will need six 2-liter bottles in the next lesson for mixing and holding pollutant solutions.

Fact Sheet: How to Use Vinegar to Imitate Acid Rain

As you know from your reading, acid rain is not vinegar. But vinegar is an acid, and you can use it to create a solution that is like acid rain. You and your teammates will need more facts.

1. How acidic should the imitation acid rain be? Here are the facts:

    ■ "Normal" rain has a pH of 5.6.

    ■ Acid rain is anything with a pH of less than 5.6.

    ■ Vinegar has a pH rating of 3.0.

    ■ To make an imitation acid rain with a pH of 4.0, you need to dilute the vinegar with water (make it weaker). For example:

      20 ml (4 tsp) of vinegar + 2 liters (2 qt) of water = imitation acid rain with a pH of 4.0

    ■ Remember, the water you begin with may have a different pH from that of normal rain. Keep this in mind when you decide how much vinegar to add. You may want to test your water's pH before deciding on your solution.

2. Now that you know the facts, discuss with your group how to set up your own experiment.

    ■ Decide how acidic to make your rain.

    ■ Figure out how much rain needs to fall each time so that it definitely gets into the aquatic ecosystem, too. Remember that you should use about the same number of dropperfuls of water that the class has been using throughout the unit to water the ecocolumn. Simply count the number of dropperfuls of pollutant solution until it begins to come out of the opening of the terrarium.

    ■ Decide how often you will schedule an acid-rain shower. Water the ecocolumn as often as the class did before. Remember, you don't want to overwater the terrarium.

    ■ Set up a recordkeeping system to keep track of this information on a daily basis (for example, a chart, calendar, or diagram).

Fact Sheet: How to Use Plant Fertilizer to Imitate Agricultural Runoff

As you know from your reading, agricultural runoff is not just chemical fertilizer. It may also include animal manure, a rich, natural fertilizer. In your experiment, you will use a fertilizer that contains many of the nutrients in both kinds of runoff.

1. How rich in nutrients should the imitation agricultural runoff be? Here are the facts:

   ■ The recommended dose is 2.5 ml (½ tsp) of fertilizer to 2 liters (2 qt) of water.

   ■ In some areas, about 10 times the recommended dose washes into the water system. This means you would add 25 ml (5 tsp) of fertilizer to 2 liters (2 qt) of water.

2. Now that you know the facts, discuss with your group how to set up your own experiment.

   ■ Decide how much fertilizer you will use.

   ■ Figure out how much fertilizer you will add each time to make sure the runoff enters the aquatic ecosystem. Remember that you should use about the same number of dropperfuls of water that the class has been using throughout the unit to water your ecocolumn.

   ■ Decide how often you will create runoff. Water the ecocolumn as often as the class did before. Remember, you don't want to overwater your terrarium.

   ■ Set up a recordkeeping system in order to keep track of this information on a daily basis (for example, a chart, calendar, or diagram).

Fact Sheet: How to Use Salt to Imitate Road Salt

The reading selection explained how we use road salt to melt ice and snow on the roads in the winter. Later, this road salt enters the soil at the side of the highways and runs off into water systems.

1. How salty should your experimental mixture be? Here are the facts:

   ■ The soil at the edge of the highway is the most heavily polluted. There you could find up to 6 ml (approx. 1¼ tsp) of salt to 1 liter (1 qt) of water.

   ■ At about 9 m from the road, expect to find about 5 ml (1 tsp) of salt to 1 liter (1 qt) of water.

   ■ At about 18 m from the road, you might find up to 3 ml (approx. ¾ tsp) of salt to 1 liter (1 qt) of water.

2. Now that you know the facts, discuss with your group how to set up your own experiment.

   ■ Decide how salty to make your solution.

   ■ Figure out how much salt and water solution you will add each time to make sure the runoff enters the aquatic ecosystem. Remember that you should use about the same number of dropperfuls of water that the class has been using throughout the unit to water your ecocolumn.

   ■ Decide how often you will apply the salt and water solution. Water the ecocolumn as often as the class did before. Remember, you don't want to overwater your terrarium.

   ■ Set up a recordkeeping system in order to keep track of this information on a daily basis (for example, a chart, a calendar, or a diagram).

Record Sheet 10-A   **Team Members**   Name: _____

                                              Name: _____

                                              Name: _____

                                              Name: _____

                                              Date: _____

Planning Worksheet

1. The pollutant we are testing is_____. We will make it by

   mixing _____ with _____ water. We will
            (amount of pollutant)   (amount of water)

   add _____ of _____ to our experimental
         (amount, in dropperfuls)   (pollutant solution)

   ecocolumn _____times per week.

2. The question we will try to answer is:

   _____

   _____

3. To make our experiment a fair test, these are the things that we will not change:

   _____

   _____

   _____

4. We will observe our experimental ecocolumn every day and record our observations. These
   are some of the things we will look for in our observations:

   _____

   _____

   _____

   _____

Record Sheet 10-A

Planning Worksheet *(continued)*

5. This is our prediction about what will happen to the plants and algae in our team's ecocolumn:

_____

_____

_____

6. This is our prediction about what will happen to the plants and algae in the class control ecocolumn:

_____

_____

_____

7. We think these things will happen because:

_____

_____

_____

Note: Give this completed sheet to your teacher.

Setting Up Our Pollution Experiments

Overview and Objectives

Following up on lessons in which they read about pollutants and designed the pollution experiments, students now implement their plans to test their hypotheses. This gives students experience in using simulations, recording results, and verifying predictions. Students apply the skills learned in Lesson 8 to observe, record, and compare results of pH testing. To establish a standard for this comparison, students use pH paper to test the ecocolumns for acidity. They analyze why the pollutant solution in their terraria has not yet affected their aquaria. In this lesson, students also discover the usefulness of varying results.

- Students test and record the pH of their ecosystems.

- Students implement their pollution experiments.

- Students mix and measure chemicals.

- Students maintain the recordkeeping system they established for their experiments.

Background

Data collection is vital to this lesson. Students have decided what type of solution they will use to pollute their experimental ecocolumns, the frequency at which they will pollute the ecocolumns, and how to recognize the effects of the pollutants. Using their plans for the pollution experiment as a guide, they will need to record their observations in their notebooks.

In this lesson, students test the pH of their team's polluted ecocolumns. By testing before polluting, students may establish that none of the ecocolumns is naturally acidic. Except for the soil in the vinegar-polluted ecocolumns, all polluted ecocolumns should be in the green range. It is unlikely that the water in the acid-polluted aquaria will test acidic at this time. Since most test results will not show acidity, you may need to point out their value. A negative result provides just as much information as a positive result.

Note: Although the soil in the ecocolumns polluted with salt or fertilizer should test in the green range, some soils are naturally acidic. Many forest soils are naturally acidic, especially those in pine, spruce, or fir forests.

Materials

For each student

1 **Record Sheet 11-A: Keeping a Record of Our Experiment**
1 science notebook

For each team

1 class ecocolumn for the pollution experiment
1 pollutant fact sheet (from Lesson 10)
1 2-liter soda bottle of water with cap (for mixing the pollutant solution)
1 funnel
1 set of measuring spoons
1 clear plastic cup
1 dropper
1 completed **Record Sheet 10-A: The Planning Worksheet**
12 5-cm (2-in) strips of pH paper

For the class

Vinegar, 500 ml (1 pt)
Salt, 450 g (1 lb)
Plant food, 240 ml (8 oz)
pH paper
1 control ecocolumn
Cleanup supplies
Newspapers to protect tabletops

Preparation

1. Make certain that you have reviewed all the students' plans for the pollution experiment before you begin this lesson.

2. Set out all supplies except the pH paper in the distribution center.

3. Cut the pH paper into 5-cm (2-in) strips. You will need twelve strips per team of four students (four strips per ecocolumn).

4. Cut at least four extra strips of pH paper so volunteers can test the control ecocolumn. Cut additional strips if there are teams of five or more in your class.

5. Make one copy of **Record Sheet 11-A: Keeping a Record of Our Experiment** for each student.

Procedure

1. Ask one team to tell the class briefly about its plan for the pollution experiment. Teams should include information on what they will do, how often they will do it, what changes they will look for, and why the class control ecocolumn is important.

2. Encourage students to ask each team questions about its plans. Clarify any points they may be unsure of before the activity begins.

3. Ask students what they remember from their experience with pH and readings and presentations about it. Let students know that to understand how pollutants might affect the acidity of their ecocolumns, they first need to test the unpolluted ecocolumns.

Figure 11-1

pH testing

4. Have students get their ecocolumns. Give each team 12 strips of pH paper and ask them to use the pH paper to test for acid. Using the color chart on the dispenser, remind students that the paper indicates how acidic a substance is: yellow is most acidic and green is least.

   ■ Test the water in the experiment's ecocolumn (touch the pH paper to the water for two seconds).

   ■ Test the soil in the experiment's ecocolumn (press the pH paper to the soil for two seconds, so that it absorbs some moisture).

   ■ Test twice to average results. Compare results.

5. Survey the class for results. Let students know they will test their experiment's ecocolumn again in this lesson.

6. Now have students pick up the supplies that they need to perform their experiments.

7. Distribute each **Record Sheet 10-A: Planning Worksheet** to its appropriate group. Distribute and review **Record Sheet 11-A: Keeping a Record of Our Experiment** to each student or use it as a model.

8. Give the teams time to conduct their pollution experiments. Check that students are following their plans, working cooperatively, measuring accurately, and recording observations in their science notebooks or on **Record Sheet 11-A.**

9. Remind students to clean up their workspaces and return all materials. Have them keep their ecocolumns for the next part of the lesson.

Final Activities

1. Ask students to discuss how they implemented their plans.

2. Now that they have polluted their ecocolumns, have students predict how the acidity may or may not have changed. Use questions such as the following:

   - How do you think polluting with fertilizer affected the pH?

   - How do you think polluting with salt affected the pH?

   - How do you think polluting with vinegar affected the pH?

3. Now ask students to test their experiment's ecocolumn for pH and compare these pH results with students' earlier ones.

4. Ask the students why, if they polluted with acid rain, the water is not acidic.

5. Ask volunteers to test the pH in both the water and soil of the class control ecocolumn (supply them with extra pH paper). Compare these results with the polluted ecocolumns. Ask students why these results may differ, particularly when comparing the control ecocolumn to the vinegar-polluted ecocolumn.

6. Have students return all ecocolumns to their assigned places.

7. Remind students to follow their plans for the pollution experiment throughout the week, and to record daily findings. They also need to water the class control ecocolumn and their own ecocolumns.

8. Collect **Record Sheets 10-A** and **11-A.**

Extensions

SCIENCE

1. Encourage students to bring in small samples of local water to test with pH paper. They might collect rainwater or snow, pond water, puddle water, or even tap water.

MATHEMATICS

2. Something that has a pH of 4 is 10 times as acidic as something that has a pH of 5. Have students use the reading selection on acid rain to determine how much more acidic vinegar is than distilled water.

Assessment

When you review **Record Sheets 11-A, 12-A,** and **13-A,** look for these points:

- Students named specific dates when they first observed changes.

- Students described observable changes.

- Students made valid inferences as to why the animals in their own ecocolumns could also be affected by pollutants.

- Students drew conclusions that reflected the facts found in their own data.

Record Sheet 11-A

Name: _____

Date: _____

Keeping a Record of Our Experiment

Keep a daily record of your experiment. Tell when you add more pollutant and how much you add. Observe both the terrarium and the aquarium in your experiment and record your observations.

	Terrarium	Aquarium
Date of Observations		
What We Did		
Amount of Pollutant Added		
pH		
Description of Plants (quantity, size, color)		
Number of Plants		
Description of Algae		
Other Observations (for example, color, odor, condition of environment)		

STC / *Ecosystems*

Observing Early Effects of Pollution

Overview and Objectives

Having conducted their pollution experiments in Lesson 11, students now evaluate the first effects of the pollutants, observing that salt and vinegar are rapidly damaging the terrarium plants. Next, by testing each aquarium's pH, students discover that one system has affected the other—a concept related to real-world land and water systems. As students revisit Lesson 7's food chain wheels, they begin to learn that what happens to producers inevitably affects consumers. These observations reinforce students' developing sensitivity toward living things.

- Students observe and record the effects pollutants have on the ecosystems used in the experiment.

- Students observe and discuss the control ecocolumn.

- Students connect the death of the producers to the viability of the consumers within the ecocolumn.

- Students state reasons why plants are important in experiments and continue to develop a sense of respect toward plants.

Background

By now you can expect the following conditions in the ecocolumns:

- The terraria should exhibit marked effects from the imitation acid rain and road salt. The plants may be yellow and wilted. Soon they may die and rot. But at this point, there probably will be no noticeable differences in the aquarium sections of these ecocolumns.

- The overfertilized terraria probably will show no noticeable effects yet.

- It will be several weeks before the pollutants from the terraria reach the aquaria in sufficient quantities to cause changes there. (A break is suggested between Lessons 12 and 13 to observe these effects.)

Students will now observe their experiments' ecocolumns for the effects of the pollutants on the plants. Afterwards, most will be able to infer that since the plants in the terraria polluted with salt and vinegar have been damaged, their crickets—had they been in the terraria—would have starved as well. The isopods are a different case; they eat dead plant matter. However, since the dead plants are probably tainted with the pollutants now, students may recognize that the isopods may have been in danger as well. This concept of cause and effect will be very important to the lesson.

Materials

For each student

1   science notebook
1   **Terrestrial Food Chain Wheel** (from Lesson 7)

For each team

1   polluted ecocolumn
2   hand lenses
1   copy of **Record Sheet 12-A: Observing Early Effects of the Pollution Experiment**
8   strips of pH paper

For the class

1   control ecocolumn
     pH paper

Preparation

1.   Cut the pH paper into 5-cm (2-in) strips. You will need eight strips per team.

2.   Duplicate one copy of **Record Sheet 12-A: Observing Early Effects of the Pollution Experiment** for each team.

3.   Organize the class so that the two teams experimenting with the same pollutant can sit together.

4.   Make certain students still have their **Terrestrial Food Chain Wheels** from Lesson 7. If not, use the blackline master on pg. 105 to remake the wheels for this lesson.

Procedure

1.   After teams pick up their polluted ecocolumns and hand lenses, ask them to describe and discuss with their team members what they see.

2.   Distribute **Record Sheet 12-A: Observing Early Effects of the Pollution Experiment** and review it with the class.

3.   Set the class control ecocolumn out in front of all groups so that one team at a time can observe the control and record observations.

4.   Pass out the pH paper.

5.   Ask students to review their notes, compare the notes with their current observations of the ecocolumns, and complete the "Observations Table" on Record Sheet 12-A. Ask each team to test the polluted ecocolumn, their own ecocolumns (containing animals), and the control ecocolumn. They will test each ecocolumn one time only. Make certain that they are using the pH paper correctly and are only using two strips per ecocolumn. Encourage them to compare pH results with the chart on the pH dispenser.

6.   Pair the two teams using the same pollutant. Challenge them to compare their teams' polluted ecocolumns with the control ecocolumn and with their own ecocolumns (containing animals).

7.   Give the two teams in each group time to complete the "Comparing Results Table" on each team's Record Sheet 12-A.

Figure 12-1

*Observing the
pollutants' effects*

8. Bring the groups together for a class discussion. Have students describe the observable effects of each pollutant. Ask each group questions such as the following:

   ■ Describe how your team's terrarium looks today. How soon after you added the pollutant did you begin to notice changes?

   ■ How does your team's terrarium compare with the other terrarium that was polluted in the same way?

   ■ Why might two ecocolumns polluted by the same pollutant show different results? One possible explanation is that one team used a stronger pollutant solution than the other.

   ■ Describe how the control terrarium looks today. Why is the control terrarium important to your experiment?

   ■ How do your own ecocolumns (unpolluted, with animals) look?

   ■ Have any of the aquaria used in the experiment changed? If so, how have they changed?

9. Ask the group working with acid rain the following questions:

   ■ What was the pH of your team's terrarium? Has this changed in any way since the last lesson?

   ■ Do you think that any acid rain has entered the aquaria used in the experiment? How can you tell?

10. Finally, ask the group working with fertilizer why it is important to record "no change."

11. Ask students to predict what will happen in their team's test ecocolumn as they continue to add pollutants over the coming weeks. Have them record predictions in their science notebooks.

12. Collect **Record Sheet 12-A.** You will need to duplicate Record Sheets 10-A, 11-A, and 12-A in Lesson 13 so that each student has a copy of his or her own team's work.

Final Activities

1. Ask students how the effects they have noted on the plants of their team's ecocolumns might have affected consumers had any been present in the the ecocolumn. Pass out the students' **Terrestrial Food Chain Wheels.** Use the following questions to focus the discussion:

   ■ In what ways did we say producers and consumers were dependent on one another in an ecosystem?

   ■ Use your food chain wheel. What would happen to the crickets if the plants were destroyed? Do you think the isopods would be in danger as well if the plants were destroyed? Explain why you feel this way.

   ■ If you were polluting your own personal ecocolumns, what do you think would eventually happen to the animals in your terraria and aquaria?

2. Be certain that the students have a keen sense of respect for living plants. Allow time for them to discuss the importance of plants in our world and in experiments such as this one.

3. Have students return the ecocolumns to their assigned place.

4. Remind students to continue to observe, record, and pollute on schedule. Remind them to continue to water their own ecocolumns and record observations.

Extensions

[SOCIAL STUDIES]   [LANGUAGE ARTS]

1. Sometimes animals have to be rescued from human-made pollution. For instance, a bird drowns if its feathers get covered with oil, and a small animal can starve if a plastic ring from a six-pack of soda gets caught around its neck. Ask students to look for stories in the news about animals rescued from human-made pollution. Put the stories on a special bulletin board.

[SOCIAL STUDIES]   [LANGUAGE ARTS]

2. Have students read a legend or myth portraying American Indian beliefs about plants (see the Bibliography).

[SCIENCE]

3. Have students create food chain wheels for their aquaria.

[MATHEMATICS]   [SOCIAL STUDIES]

4. Provide students with graphs on ecology; for example, one that shows the changing populations of various endangered species. You can also provide maps; for example, one illustrating the rate of decline of rain forests in South America. Have students analyze these graphs and maps.

Assessment

1. The first two **Final Activities** can help you assess students' understanding of the following:

    ■ The definitions of "producer" and "consumer" and how organisms interrelate in an environment

    ■ The effects pollutants have on producers and consumers

    ■ Why plants are vital to the food chain

    These Final Activities should also help you assess students' sensitivity toward living things.

2. Let students design and carry out an experiment on their own. This will help you assess each student's abilities. Have students set up a fair test to find out if an ice cube with salt on it melts faster than one with no salt on it. To evaluate their experiment, look for the following:

    ■ A systematic approach

    ■ Appropriate use of equipment

    ■ The use of controls such as starting at the same time or setting up the ice cubes in the same location

    ■ An attempt to quantify the sizes of the ice cubes

    ■ An attempt to time the melting process

    ■ Recordkeeping

Management Tip

Wait three to four days before starting on Lesson 13, in which students will observe the escalating effects of their pollution experiments. The longer you wait between lessons, the more pronounced those effects will be.

During this break you may want your students to engage in activities similar to the one listed in Assessment 2 above. Such activities test your students' abilities to set up scientific experiments. Use the Bibliography to find books on other experimental activities.

Record Sheet 12-A

Observing Early Effects of the Pollution Experiment

Your names (Team 1):

Other team's names (Team 2):

_____

_____

_____

_____

_____

_____

_____

_____

Teams' pollutant: _____

Date: _____

Observations Table

	Your Terrarium Used in the Experiment	Class Control Terrarium	Your Aquarium Used in the Experiment	Class Control Aquarium
pH				
Color (soil, water)				
Plants and Algae (for example, number, length, color)				
Other Observations				

How does the class control ecocolumn compare with your ecocolumn used in the experiment?

How do you explain these similarities and differences?

Record Sheet 12-A   Name: _____

Observing Early Effects of the Pollution Experiment *(continued)*

Comparing Results Table

	Team 1's Ecocolumn Used in the Experiment	Team 2's Ecocolumn Used in the Experiment
Amount of Pollutant Solution		
Frequency of Watering with Pollutant		
What we Observed in the Terrarium		
What we Observed in the Aquarium		

How are the two teams' ecocolumns the same?

How are the two teams' ecocolumns different?

How do you explain any differences in your ecocolumns if you were using the same pollutant?

LESSON 13

Where Do the Pollutants Go?

Overview and Objectives

Reflecting on their experiences as experimenters in Lesson 12, students now focus on how scientists use models to answer questions. By comparing the results of their experiments, students also learn the importance of using controls and averaging data. Finally, as students observe the pollutants' escalating effects, they conclude that the pollutants have seeped through the soil and into the water. From their observations, students infer that water pollution endangers aquatic animals.

- Student teams discuss the effects of pollutants on their ecosystems and make final observations.

- Student teams review the data collected from the pollution experiments.

- Student teams use their data to draw and support conclusions.

Background

Although the damage to the terrestrial system was visible almost immediately (particularly in the acid-polluted columns), it took longer for damage to become visible in the aquatic system. In real-world ecosystems, this is often the case as well. Frequently, the pollutants have accumulated over a long period of time before the damage shows.

Today you can expect to find some of the following conditions:

- In the terraria polluted with acid and salt, no healthy plants remain.

- In the overfertilized terraria, plants probably are thriving.

- In all three cases, pollutants have begun to build up in the aquaria. Therefore, in the aquaria treated with acid and salt, plants may be discolored. Water in the overfertilized aquaria may look greener, indicating an increase in algae.

When they realize that the pollutants are affecting the aquaria too, students may infer that had their own personal ecocolumns (containing animals) been used in the pollution experiments, the animals also would have been in danger. It is important that students make some inferences about how each pollutant could affect organisms in real-life situations.

Students may find the data-analysis portion of the lesson a challenge, but it is a necessary scientific exercise. Until now, students have simply been recording observable details, such as the number of aquatic plants, plant size, and pH. Now it is time for students to make inferences using these recorded data.

As they review their own records and draw conclusions about the experiments, they will use the same process that professional scientists use to make sense of their data. You might point this out to help students realize how vital recordkeeping is to the experimental process.

It is important, too, that those teams experimenting with the same pollutant compare their data. Scientists often repeat their experiments many times and compare their results with those of others working on the same experiment.

More data make a more convincing case. For example, if both teams experimenting with acid rain observed that terrarium plants turned yellow after two days, the data are significant. The next lesson will focus again on the class's collective data.

Materials

For each student
- 1 science notebook
- 1 completed copy of **Record Sheet 12-A: Observing Early Effects of the Pollution Experiments**
- 1 completed copy of **Record Sheet 11-A: Keeping a Record of Our Experiment**
- 1 completed copy of **Record Sheet 10-A: Planning Worksheet**
- 1 copy of **Record Sheet 13-A: Analyzing the Results of the Pollution Experiment**

For each team
- 1 polluted ecocolumn
- 1 cup
- 2 hand lenses

For the class
- 1 control ecocolumn

Preparation

1. Duplicate one **Record Sheet 13-A: Analyzing the Results of the Pollution Experiment** for each student.

2. Duplicate each completed record sheet (Record Sheets 10-A, 11-A, and 12-A) so that each student has a copy of his or her own team's work from Lessons 10 through 12.

3. Organize the class so that teams experimenting with the same pollutant can sit together.

Procedure

1. Ask students to pick up their ecocolumns and supplies and sit with the other group of students experimenting with the same pollutant. Discuss what they see.

2. Distribute copies of the past record sheets to the appropriate team members. Ask students to review their records.

3. After students record observations and changes, have them describe these to the class.

4. Set out the control ecocolumn. Now, ask students to discuss the implications of observable changes in the ecocolumns.

   ■ Compare the terraria polluted in the same way. What similarities do you see? What differences?

   ■ Compare the control terrarium and aquarium to the experimental ones. What is the evidence that the pollutants have reached the aquaria?

   ■ What might have happened to the animals living in your own individual aquaria and terraria had these ecosystems also been polluted? What evidence do you have to support this inference?

5. Ask students to return all supplies and to put the ecocolumns back in their assigned places.

6. Distribute **Record Sheet 13-A: Analyzing the Results of the Pollution Experiment** and go over it with the class. Mention these points:

   ■ Students should refer to their own record sheets and notebook observations when filling out Record Sheet 13-A. Point out that this is what professional scientists do.

   ■ Encourage the teams experimenting with the same pollutant to discuss the questions with each other, but ask each student to complete an individual record sheet.

   ■ Help students use their original planning worksheets to complete questions 1, 2, and 9. Make sure that they are clear about the difference between first observations and observations made over time. Finally, encourage the two teams that used the same pollutant to discuss their results and refer back to **Record Sheet 12-A** before answering question 10.

7. Collect the completed copies of Record Sheet 13-A.

Final Activities

1. Ask students to plan a report that briefly discusses their experimental results. They will give these reports in Lesson 14. After that, the whole class will try to make some inferences about the effects of each pollutant on the organisms in the ecocolumns and about how these pollutants could also affect animals.

2. Remind students to continue to water their own ecosystems on schedule.

Extensions

SOCIAL STUDIES

1. Have students find a feather and dip it in oil. Then have them try to clean it off. Is it difficult? Discuss how different kinds of human-made pollutants affect birds in real life.

SCIENCE

2. Do a class experiment to see how quickly a plant absorbs a pollutant. Put a white carnation into a vase. Add a couple of drops of red food coloring to one of the pollutant solutions. Place the solution in the vase and observe the carnation for a couple of days. Discuss what happens.

Record Sheet 13-A

Name: _____

Date: _____

Analyzing the Results of the Pollution Experiment

You and your teammates have collected a great deal of information about how your team's ecocolumn was affected by the pollutant you added to it. Like all scientists, you need to organize and analyze your data and decide what it means.

Use your team's planning worksheet and other record sheets or daily notebook observations to answer the following questions. Remember to use specific dates and recorded scientific observations to support your answers.

1. What question did you try to answer with your experiment?

   _____

   _____

2. What parts of your plan did you follow and what parts didn't you follow? (For example, did you water on schedule?)

   _____

   _____

   _____

   _____

3. What were the first changes you noticed in the terrarium that you used in the experiment? When did you first observe these changes?

   _____

   _____

   _____

4. Describe the changes over time that you observed in the terrarium used in the experiment.

   _____

   _____

   _____

   _____

Record Sheet 13-A

Analyzing the Results of the Pollution Experiment *(continued)*

5. Knowing what happened to the plants in the experiment's terrarium, what do you think would have happened to the crickets and isopods in your own ecocolumn if it had been polluted?

_____

_____

_____

_____

6. What were the first changes you noticed in the experiment's aquarium? When did you first observe these changes?

_____

_____

_____

_____

7. Describe the changes you observed in the aquarium over time.

_____

_____

_____

_____

8. Knowing what happened to the organisms in the aquarium used in the experiment, what do you think would have happened to the mosquito fish and snails in your own ecocolumn if it had been polluted?

_____

_____

_____

_____

Record Sheet 13-A

Analyzing the Results of the Pollution Experiment *(continued)*

9. Look again at your answer to question 1 on this record sheet. What is the answer to your experimental question?

_____

_____

_____

_____

10. How do the results of your team's experiment compare with the results of the other team doing the same experiment?

_____

_____

_____

_____

Drawing Conclusions about Our Experiment

Overview and Objectives

In this lesson, students conclude their pollution experiments. They begin relating the results of their own experiments to the pollution problems that exist in land and water systems on earth. After reporting on the experiments, pooling all the teams' data, and examining the data, students draw conclusions about the effects of each pollutant. By reading about a real ecosystem in danger, the Chesapeake Bay, they start exploring ways to solve real-life environmental problems.

- Students report on their team experiments.

- The class pools and analyzes its data on the effects of each pollutant.

- The class draws conclusions about the effects of each pollutant.

- Students examine discrepant results.

- Students read about the Chesapeake Bay.

Background

The process students use to reach their conclusions today is more important than the conclusions themselves. Students have followed the process that scientists use the world over: ask a question, conduct an experiment, collect data, analyze the data, and draw a conclusion. But as they will soon discover, the results of an experiment are not always clear-cut. While students all will agree on some points, they will argue about others. This is appropriate, because it is also what happens in professional experimental labs.

Differing results are an important part of science experimentation because they lead to deeper thinking on a question. Sometimes they compel one scientist to repeat an experiment in an effort to replicate another's results. Sometimes they lead a scientist to design a new and different experiment to answer the same question. Sometimes, they lead to new questions.

This lesson ends with a reading selection on the Chesapeake Bay. The reading selection serves two purposes:

- It links the students' classroom pollution experiments to a real-world ecosystem. Students will begin to discover that the Chesapeake Bay, like all ecosystems, is a complex system with complex problems.

- It gives students the general background information they will need to make their presentations on the bay in Lesson 16.

Management Tip: Because this is a long lesson, you may want to integrate the Chesapeake Bay reading selection into your language arts or social studies time. Or, you may want to assign it as homework.

Materials

For each student

1   science notebook
1   completed **Record Sheet 13-A: Analyzing the Results of the Pollution Experiment**

For the class

3   sheets of newsprint or transparency film and markers
    Living on the Edge, a video about the Chesapeake Bay
    VHS player and television monitor

Preparation

1.   Obtain the materials for recording student ideas.

2.   Label the top half of each of the three sheets, respectively, "What We Found Out about the Effects of Acid Rain," "What We Found Out about the Effects of Road Salt," and "What We Found Out about the Effects of Overfertilization." On the bottom half of each sheet, write "What We Predict Would Happen to the Animals in an Ecosystem Polluted with Acid Rain," and so forth.

     Subdivide each sheet into "Terrarium" and "Aquarium" (see Figure 14-1).

3.   Decide how best to include the film about the Chesapeake Bay, *Living on the Edge*, and the reading selection in your class's schedule.

Procedure

1.   Ask a team from each group to report the findings from their experiment.

2.   Record findings on the sheets. Then ask the other team from each group if they agree, disagree, or want to add new information. Have the students add "agree" or "disagree" to the findings on the sheets.

3.   Proceed until the data has been contributed on all three pollutants.

4.   Help students draw some conclusions.

     ■   Reread the three sheets with the class and circle the statements that show total agreement. These represent conclusions backed up by two teams' collective data.

     ■   Next, look for the disputed points. Ask students to suggest ways they could clear up the dispute. Two solutions would be either to redo the experiment or to design new experiments to answer the question (see Extension 1 on pg. 160).

     ■   Ask students for reasons why the results differed.

5.   Now have students predict what might happen to the animals in an ecosystem polluted with each substance. Record their answers on the bottom half of each sheet.

6.   Help students discuss their predictions.

     ■   Circle statements that agree.

     ■   Look for the disputed points.

     ■   Ask students to explain why these predictions might differ.

Figure 14-1

Charting the results of the pollution experiments

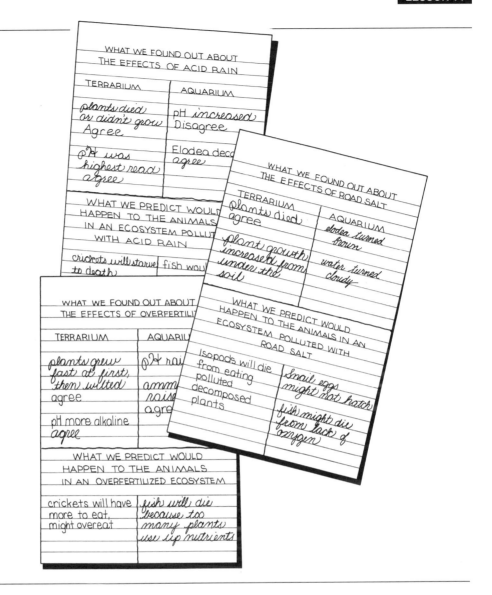

Final Activities

1. Introduce the reading selection on the Chesapeake Bay (pg. 69 in the Student Activity Book and pg. 161 in this guide). A few questions may help students focus their reading.

   ■ What are the main problems in the Chesapeake Bay?

   ■ How are the Chesapeake Bay's problems similar to the problems you experienced with your team's polluted ecocolumns (or would have experienced if your own ecocolumns were polluted)?

   ■ Describe a situation where too much of something is going into the bay.

   ■ Describe a situation where too much of something is being taken out of the bay.

   ■ After completing the reading selection, describe another ecosystem that is similar to the Chesapeake Bay.

   Let the class know you will discuss these questions in the next lesson. Ask that they record any thoughts on these items in their science notebooks.

2. Remind students to continue to make and record observations and water their ecocolumns as needed.

3. Show the videotape *Living on the Edge.* Discuss the following:

- What supports much of the life in the bay?

- How have the millions of people who have moved into the bay area affected it?

- In what ways do people use the bay? In what ways have people damaged the bay?

Note: The videotape is supplied in the kit from Carolina Biological Supply Company. It is also available from the Chesapeake Bay Foundation (see Bibliography).

Extensions

> SCIENCE

1. Challenge students to design a new experiment to resolve a disputed point from today's lesson. If possible, have them carry out the new experiment.

> LANGUAGE ARTS

2. Invite students to write a story in which one of the characters "jumps to a conclusion" that is not necessarily the right one.

> LANGUAGE ARTS   SOCIAL STUDIES

3. Encourage students to do library research to find out more about the Chesapeake Bay, San Francisco Bay, or other bays around the U.S. (see the Bibliography for suggested resources on the Chesapeake Bay).

Reading Selection

The Chesapeake Bay: An Ecosystem in Danger

Exploring the Bay in 1608, Captain John Smith found a bounteous bay full of fish such as "brettes, mullets, white Salmonds, Trowts, Soles, Plaice, Herrings, Rockfish, Eeles, Shades, Crabs, Shrimps, Oysters, Cocles and Muscles.... In somer," he wrote, "no place affordeth more plentie of Sturgeon, nor in winter more abundance of fowle.... In the small rivers all the years there is good plentie of small fish, so that with hookes those that would take paines had sufficient."*

The Chesapeake Bay Is an Ecosystem

The Chesapeake Bay area is a vast and complicated ecosystem. It covers a surface area of over 2,200 square miles (approximately 3,500 square kilometers). That's almost as large as the entire state of Delaware! Its waters are a mixture of fresh water from about 150 rivers and streams and salt water from the Atlantic Ocean. The bay holds 18 trillion gallons of water!

The bay bursts with all kinds of life. Its producers include water grasses anchored to the bottom and algae so tiny you need a microscope to see one. And its animals range from crabs, fish, muskrats, and seahorses to swans, diamondback terrapins, and billions of baby eels.

Over 13 million people live, work, and play in the Chesapeake Bay watershed.

The land around the Chesapeake is a jumble of different environments: swamps, wetlands, meadows, forests, mountains, and beaches. Each environment is home to many different kinds of plants and animals. In fact, over 2,500 different kinds of plants and animals live in the bay area.

In the bay's ecosystem (as in all ecosystems) every single element—water, land, air, light, and living things—is connected in a complex web of relationships. For the bay area, the web is very complex indeed.

But remember: through your work on the ecocolumns, you have already learned a lot about ecosystems. This will help you understand the complicated ecosystem of the Chesapeake Bay.

How Is the Bay Like Your Ecosystem?

You have seen that what happens on land (as in your terrarium) can greatly affect what happens in water (as in your aquarium). Now apply this idea to the land bordering the Chesapeake. It's covered with farms and factories, cities and highways, schools and apartment buildings, landfills and campgrounds, restaurants and marinas.

---

* Eugene L. Meyer, *Maryland Lost and Found: Peoples and Places from Chesapeake to Appalachia* (Baltimore: The Johns Hopkins University Press, 1986).

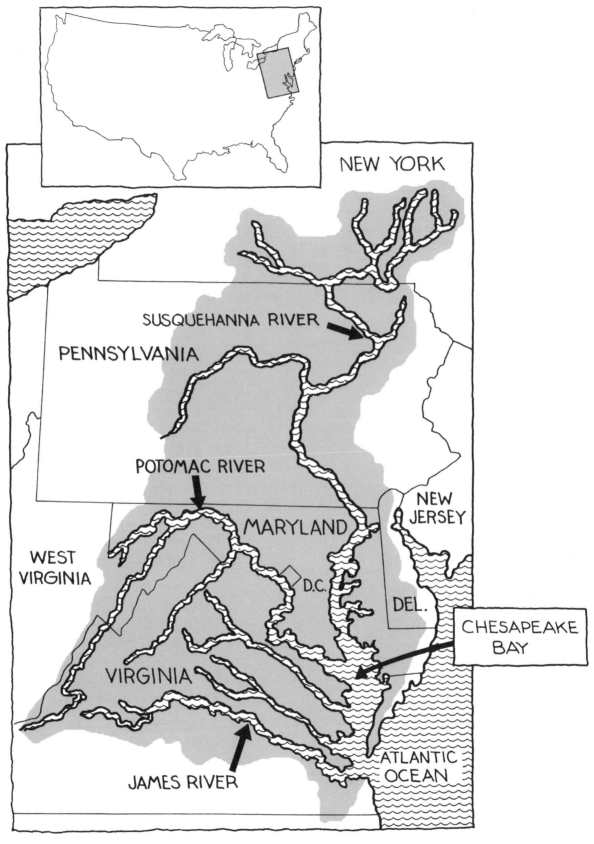

Chesapeake Bay watershed area

Over 13 million people live, work, and play there. One way or another, pollutants from all of these people wind up in the bay's waters.

So, what if a homeowner in the Chesapeake area overfertilizes his or her lawn? That extra fertilizer eventually washes into the Chesapeake Bay. The same goes for the road salt used after a snow storm. And what about the acid rain caused by industry, homes, and cars? Where do you think it goes?

What Is a Watershed?
An area of land whose waters all drain into the same place is a **watershed.** You could think of your terrarium as the watershed for your aquarium. The Chesapeake Bay's watershed is huge. As you can see from the map, it drains water from six states (Maryland, Delaware, Pennsylvania, Virginia, West Virginia, and New York) and the District of Columbia. It covers 64,000 square miles between Vermont and North Carolina.

It's All Downhill
Think about this. The land in this watershed slopes toward the bay the way the inside of a bathtub slopes toward its drain. So, much of the water that runs off this land flows down the slope, toward the bay. Just imagine industrial waste pouring out of Baltimore's factories, puddles of motor oil on the highway, extra fertilizer and pesticides from lawns in Virginia and Delaware, muddy runoff from construction sites in Maryland, acid runoff from mines in West Virginia, cow manure from Pennsylvania dairy farms, and sewage from 13 million people's toilets. Sooner or later, it all flows toward the bay.

With all this human-made pollution, no wonder the bay is in trouble.

A Problem: Too Much Goes into the Bay, Too Much Comes Out

The ecological problem in the Chesapeake Bay has two main causes: people are putting too many pollutants into the bay; and people

are "overharvesting," or taking too much seafood out of the bay.

Let's take a closer look at each cause. How does each affect the bay and all the living things in it?

Too Many Pollutants

From your team's ecocolumns, you know that pollutants in an ecosystem can set off a chain of events. For example, what happens when pollution kills plants? You may also have predicted that if there were animals in your team's ecocolumns, the animals—who depended on those plants—would have starved. This has happened in the Chesapeake.

Too many nutrients from human sewage, cow manure, and fertilizer are overloading the bay. This causes **algae blooms.** Too many algae cloud the water and keep light from reaching the grass below. What's the result? Underwater grass beds are dying fast.

The Importance of Grass
The grass beds are essential to the bay's health. When nutrients wash in, the grasses take them in and use them to grow. Also, the roots of the grasses help hold down the bay's muddy bottom. That way, mud doesn't get stirred up, cloud the water, and block the sunlight.

Grass beds near the shoreline help absorb the pounding of the waves. This helps keep the soil there from washing away. When the grass beds do their job, the water stays clearer, sunlight pours in, and other aquatic plants thrive.

Animals need underwater grasses, too. Ducks, geese, swans, snails, isopods, worms, muskrats, beavers, sea slugs, and other animals of the bay depend on the grasses for food. In the bay's grass beds, baby fish, shrimp, crabs, seahorses, and even turtles stay safe. What will happen to these animals if the grass beds disappear?

Underwater grass beds are home to many living things.

Sediment Kills

Did you notice that when you watered your terrarium enough to cause a runoff, the runoff was cloudy? That's because it contained not only water but also tiny bits of soil, called **sediment.** Some sedimentation occurs naturally. But humans cause most of it, especially when we cut down trees and other vegetation.

Forests help keep sediment out of the Chesapeake. Tree roots help hold the soil in place. Their leaves and branches cushion rainfall so it hits the ground more gently. (Then the soil and roots have time to absorb the water.) Leaf matter on the forest floor acts like a sponge. Leaves soak up the water and slow its flow.

But we've cut down about 40 percent of the forests in the Chesapeake watershed to build highways, houses, shopping centers, and offices. Unlike forests, these hard surfaces (such as pavements and rooftops) prevent water from seeping slowly into the soil. When it rains, water races off these surfaces, picks up more sediment (and whatever it holds, such as pesticides or chemicals from asphalt roof tiles), and gushes toward the bay.

Like algae, sediment clouds the water and keeps light from reaching the underwater plants. It also can clog fish gills and smother fish eggs. Bottom dwellers such as clams, oysters, worms, sponges, and coral can smother under a layer of sediment.

What Happens to the Animals?

Oysters: Nature's Filters

Oysters serve as natural filters, helping keep the water clear. To trap its food, microscopic algae, an oyster pumps in water—up to two gallons per hour! Along with the algae, oysters suck in sediment that would otherwise cloud the water. Oysters pump the clear water back out. Then they digest the algae and drop harmless pellets of waste (which include sediment) to the bottom of the bay.

In Colonial times, the floor of the Chesapeake Bay was piled high with oyster beds. In fact, ships had to be careful to steer around them. But today, only 1 percent of the oysters are left. And they can no longer play a big part in keeping the water clear.

Oysters: nature's filters

This is also bad news for the snails, crabs, and small fish that live in the millions of nooks and crannies in a healthy oyster bed. Many of these creatures lost their homes.

What happened to all the Chesapeake's oysters? A virus infected some of them. Pollution killed others. And oyster drill snails ate still more. But the main reason so few oysters are left is that people have eaten most of them.

Lots of people find oysters so tasty that they will pay a high price for them. So it is no surprise that watermen are taking so many out of the bay. As a result, not enough oysters are left to replenish the population.

Go Fish

Many different kinds of fish live in or visit the Chesapeake Bay for part of the year. Some have unusual names, like cownose ray or hogchoker. But you may have heard of others, such as shad, rockfish (striped bass), herring, perch, eel, and bluefish. Some eat plants and algae. Some are bottom feeders and hunt in oyster or grass beds for snails, small crabs, and worms. Some eat smaller fish.

Fish that visit the bay for only part of the year seem to be doing fine. But fish that live there year-round may be in trouble. In fact, the rockfish population has been so low that some states, such as Maryland, have laws to control fishing for rockfish.

Why are fisherman catching fewer fish? There are many reasons. People built dams across the rivers in the bay's watershed area. And these stop fish from swimming upstream to lay eggs. Cars and power plants that use fossil fuels have caused acid rain. It has damaged both eggs and young fish. Harmful chemicals from factories and mines can give fish cancer or even kill them. Plus, there is the sediment that can kill fish eggs and clog fish gills.

And remember, one of the bay's biggest problems is that we take too much out of it. For most kinds of fish, there are no limits on how many can be caught. So commercial fishermen (who catch fish for a living) and sports fishermen continue to overfish the bay.

Blue Crabs: The Last Great Catch

The Chesapeake Bay still produces about half of the nation's blue crab harvest. They are the last great catch in the bay. As fish and oysters become scarcer, the demand for crabs grows. Watermen can sell just about as many as they can pull out of the water.

Blue crabs are real survivors. They are scavengers who eat almost anything they can find. In spite of pollution, changes in temperature, and more salt in the water, the blue crabs live on.

But even the blue crab is showing signs of trouble. As the grass beds disappear, crabs are losing their safest hiding place. (To avoid being eaten during molting, for example, crabs need to hide in the grass while their shells harden.) And as the oyster beds disappear, young crabs are losing their winter homes.

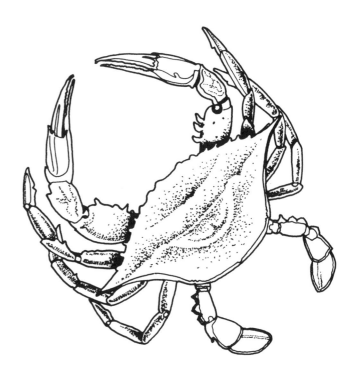

Blue crabs are the last great catch in the bay.

Searching for Solutions

If the animals in your ecocolumns had been threatened by pollution, the solution would have been simple: move them to a safe place. In the real world of the Chesapeake Bay, the problems are much more complex. And the solutions are, too.

Everyone agrees that the Chesapeake Bay has many problems, most of them human-made. But depending on where they live and what they do, people who live, work, and play in the Chesapeake Bay watershed area see these problems from very different points of view. And what seems like a solution to one group may seem like a problem to another group.

Let's look at the bay's problems from several different points of view. Then let's see if we can come up with some solutions. We all know that solving problems requires making compromises. That means we often need to give up one thing to receive another. This is called a **trade-off.** Both groups work together to do what is best. Depending on your point of view, you will find some solutions and trade-offs more difficult to live with than others. Each group will need to decide how it can best help the bay without giving up too much.

Examining a Real Environmental Problem

Overview and Objectives

Having read about the Chesapeake Bay, an ecosystem in danger, students now use role-playing to examine the bay from different points of view: the ordinary citizen, dairy farmer, waterman, land developer, and recreational boater. By completing a problem-solving sheet, student groups analyze the bay's problems from one of these perspectives, propose solutions, and identify trade-offs involved in such solutions.

- Students work in groups to define a problem from different points of view.

- Students identify possible solutions to pollution problems.

- Students define the term "trade-off" and identify the trade-offs involved in specific solutions.

Background

Several of the Chesapeake Bay's pollution problems (overfertilization, acid rain, and road salt runoff) mirror those in the class's experiments. And since students now know more about the sources and effects of various pollutants, they are better equipped to analyze the bay situation from different perspectives and to suggest workable solutions. The frustrating part, as they will soon discover, is that no one group has the answer to all of the bay's problems.

It will be challenging for students to grapple with the trade-offs involved in their proposed solutions. Many may find it difficult to realize that what seems to be in the best interest of their group may not be in the best interest of the bay—and vice versa. If your students are unable to grasp the concept of trade-off, use several daily scenarios to illustrate it. (Example: You want to go to the park. Your friend wants to play a new video game in his apartment. You decide to play the video game. The trade-off is that you give up going to the park—a disadvantage to you—but you still enjoy your friend's company and learn to play a new game in return.)

All the information presented in the point of view sheets at the end of this lesson was based on interviews with real people closely connected to the interest groups represented. (See the Acknowledgments on pgs. v–vi to get a sense of the information sources used.) Please also note that the term "waterman" is the accepted term used by the Maryland Watermen's Association and other waterman groups. It is used to refer to both men and women.

Management Tip: In discussing, organizing, and presenting a problem, students will use many different skills, including language and problem-solving skills. For this reason, you may find it useful to integrate the next two lessons into your language arts program.

Materials

For each student
   1   point of view sheet

For each team of students
   1   **Record Sheet 15-A: Problem-Solving Sheet**
   1   sheet of newsprint (or space on the chalkboard) and a marker

Preparation

1. Divide the class into five teams of four to six students each. Assign each team a point of view to represent: ordinary citizen, dairy farmer, waterman, land developer, or recreational boater. (Or, let students volunteer or draw lots.)

2. Duplicate four to six copies of each point of view sheet.

3. Review **Record Sheet 15-A: Problem-Solving Sheet.** Duplicate one sheet per group.

4. This is a long lesson. Decide if you would like to divide it into two parts. A suggested stopping point is at the end of the **Procedure** section.

Procedure

1. Ask the class to identify the key points in the reading selection on the Chesapeake Bay. Encourage students to share their notebook entries from Lesson 14's **Final Activities.**

2. After asking a volunteer to read aloud the last paragraph of Lesson 14's reading selection, invite students to come up with their own definition of "trade-off."

3. Involve students in brainstorming examples from daily living that illustrate trade-offs.

4. Distribute the point of view sheets and explain how the sheets will be used. Allow students time to read the sheets.

5. Then have groups meet and discuss their particular view of the bay's environmental problems. As they meet, they need to consider these topics:

   ■ From your group's point of view, what are the main environmental problems? How do you contribute to these problems?

   ■ What could your group do to help solve the environmental problems in the bay? Think of as many solutions as you can.

   ■ Think about what your group gets from the bay. Some of the solutions might require your group to give up something. But other groups and the bay might benefit. This is a "trade-off." For each solution your group proposes, discuss the trade-offs.

6. Distribute **Record Sheet 15-A** to each group and go over it with the class. Emphasize that students should use their own words to fill out the record sheet and not the words of the point of view sheets.

7. Have students fill out Record Sheet 15-A, one per group.

8. Collect Record Sheet 15-A to make certain that each group has identified the solutions and trade-offs. Then redistribute the record sheets before Step 4 in the **Final Activities.**

Management Tip: If you choose to divide this lesson into two parts, this is a good place to stop.

Final Activities

1. Alert students that in the next class they will hold a mini-conference on the Chesapeake Bay. During the mini-conference, they will make presentations on the following:

   ■ How their group contributes to the bay's problems

   ■ The solutions they propose

   ■ The trade-offs involved in some of the solutions (including advantages to the bay and disadvantages to the group, or vice versa)

   These presentations can be as elaborate or as simple as you and your class care to make them. Here are some basic suggestions:

   ■ Give each group a large sheet of newsprint or provide board space where students can transfer their information from **Record Sheet 15-A.**

   ■ Have each group divide its presentation into four to six manageable tasks. For example:

     ■ One student states the problem as that group sees it.

     ■ One student lists the group's proposed solutions.

     ■ One student describes the advantages of each solution to the bay.

     ■ One student describes the disadvantages to the group.

2. Once you have discussed these minimum requirements, suggest that students adopt different styles to make the presentations more interesting. For example:

   ■ The presentation could take the form of a panel discussion.

   ■ Students could debate the advantages and disadvantages of different solutions to the bay's problems.

   ■ Students could hold a meeting of their special interest group (for example, a boating club) to discuss the bay's problems.

   ■ Reporters could interview persons from various points of view (see Extension 3).

3. Now that your class has decided what form the presentations will take for the mini-conference, discuss ways to turn it into a memorable event. For example:

   ■ Invite guests. These might be another class, parents, or the principal.

   ■ Publicize the mini-conference. Have the class give it a title. Notify the school newspaper, send notes home, and hang posters.

   ■ Use props to enhance the presentations. These might include maps, audiovisual equipment (such as an overhead transparency and projector, a tape recorder and microphone, a video camera), models (such as farms, boats, housing developments, crabs, oysters), or "official" identification badges.

   ■ Wear costumes.

4. Now give your students time to research and prepare for Lesson 16's presentations.

Extensions

1. Have students write invitations to the mini-conference. Or, they could write and illustrate a news article for the school paper.

ART

2. Artwork can really dress up a presentation. Encourage students to draw pictures or maps, make models, create collages, or design displays to use in their presentations.

LANGUAGE ARTS   SOCIAL STUDIES

3. Assign several students to be reporters at the mini-conference. A reporter could interview students representing conflicting points of view and then publish an article in the class newspaper. Or, students can handle the interview as if it were for radio or television.

Point of View Sheet: Ordinary Citizens

Your group will represent the point of view of an ordinary citizen living in the Chesapeake Bay watershed area. People going about the normal business of their daily lives all have an effect on the area in which they live.

After you have read the selection, discuss these questions with the rest of your group as if you were a citizen of the bay area:

- In your own words, how do you think you, as an ordinary citizen, contribute to the problems in the Chesapeake Bay?

- How could the different members of your family help solve the bay's problems?

- What solutions would be difficult to live with?

- What benefits would you get from a healthier bay?

From an Ordinary Citizen's Point of View

Here are two quotes from ordinary citizens of the bay area:

My big sister washes her hair two times a day! I tell her she's using up too much hot water. That's wasting energy.

This year when I voted for my Maryland state representative, I looked closely at all the candidates' stands on environment. I voted for the one who had some really good ideas about saving the Chesapeake Bay.

Hundreds of thousands of people live, work, play, and go to school in the Chesapeake Bay watershed area. Some live in apartment buildings or private homes in cities like Baltimore, Maryland; Wilmington, Delaware; and Washington, D.C. Others live in suburbs or small towns. Still others make their homes in the country.

And they do many different things to make a living. Some spend a lot of time working outside on farms, boats, construction sites, shipyards, or parks. Others work inside in factories, hospitals, schools, offices, shops, restaurants, museums, or theaters.

Wherever they make their homes, many people in the area enjoy the excitement of city life. Others like to get away from it all and spend time on or near the waters of the Chesapeake Bay.

How People Contribute to the Bay's Problems

All people living in the Chesapeake watershed area create pollutants. In some way or another, these pollutants eventually reach the bay. As a citizen of the bay, here are some problems you might create:

■ You produce garbage and sewage.

■ You drive cars, trucks, buses, lawnmowers, and boats. All of these produce exhaust that adds to air pollution.

■ You use energy in the form of gas and electricity to run appliances, operate televisions and radios, open garage doors, and heat, cool, and light your homes. This energy from fossil fuels creates air pollution and contributes to acid rain.

How People Can Help the Bay

Everyone can do his or her part to help the Chesapeake Bay. If you were a citizen of the Chesapeake Bay area, here is just a sampling of things you could do to save energy. You will probably think of many more.

■ Use less energy. Lower the thermostat in winter and turn it up in the summer. Walk, ride a bike, carpool, or use public transportation. Turn off lights when you leave a room.

■ Save water. Take shorter showers. Don't let the water run when you brush your teeth. Fix leaky faucets. Run the dishwasher only when it is full. Install water-saving toilets and shower heads. Plant trees and grasses that don't need watering.

■ Produce less trash. Recycle glass, metal, aluminum, paper, and motor oil. Reuse old materials or donate them to someone

who will. Avoid buying disposable items. Compost leaves and food scraps and turn them into valuable soil.

■ Stop using toxic products like chemical weed killers or insecticides. Pull weeds by hand and select plants that resist insects.

■ Stop using chemical fertilizers on lawns and gardens. Investigate organic gardening.

■ Dispose of toxic materials properly at designated community disposal sites (such as a local car service center or paint store). Never pour poisons like paint, oil, or antifreeze down the sink drain, onto the ground, or down a storm drain.

■ Support elected officials who are in favor of laws to protect the bay. Then let these officials know what you think by calling them or writing letters to express your concerns.

■ Learn more about how to save the bay and share what you learn with others.

■ Join a group to take action on any one of the bay's problems. There are many responsible organizations working hard to improve the Chesapeake Bay.

Trade-offs: Advantages for the Bay and Disadvantages for the Group

Sometimes what is good for the environment is hard on people. Reread each suggestion about how ordinary people could help the bay, and then ask yourself these questions:

■ How would this solution help improve the bay?

■ What are the trade-offs involved in this solution?

Point of View Sheet: Land Developers

Your group will represent the point of view of land developers in the Chesapeake Bay area. Developers make their living by planning and building homes, roads, shopping centers, and office buildings. Besides supplying us with the structures we need, developers also provide many jobs.

After you have read the selection, discuss these questions with the rest of your group as if you were a land developer in the bay area:

- In your own words, how do you think you, as land developers, contribute to the problems in the Chesapeake Bay?

- How could you help solve the bay's problems?

- Which solutions would be hard on you?

- What benefits would you get from a healthier bay?

From the Land Developers' Point of View

Here are two quotes from land developers in the bay area:

Sure the Chesapeake Bay is a beautiful area. That's why people want to live there. By building homes on the waterfront, we're simply giving folks what they want. Filling a need.

We want another highway built outside of Washington, D.C. And maybe in the long run it's bad news for the bay. But have you ever gotten stuck in rush hour traffic on your way out of D.C.? I've never seen so many cars! Commuters are begging for another highway.

Land development in the entire Chesapeake watershed area is a big business. It involves thousands of people in many different kinds of jobs: buying and selling land, planning what to build, designing the buildings, constructing them, decorating, landscaping, loaning money, and writing legal contracts, to name just a few. As they see it, the developer's job is simply to provide what people moving into the Chesapeake area want: affordable housing, good roads, convenient shopping, offices, and schools.

Of course, land developers have to follow rules about what they can build, where they can build it, and how many buildings they can put there. Other rules tell how a neighborhood should look, such as how wide the streets can be and where the houses can go. Plus they have to follow rules that help prevent pollution (like the soil that can wash off construction sites after rain storms).

Many developers claim that these rules are too strict and that they cost too much to follow. But other people say that even stricter codes are needed to protect the bay.

The Chesapeake Bay area is a very desirable place to live. Some think that too many people already live there and that development should be strictly limited. But right now, more people continue to move in every day.

So, every day more farmland is turned into housing tracts. More forests are cleared and paved over. And more wetlands are filled in. Wherever people move in, much of the wildlife moves out. So, many different species of both plants and animals are rapidly losing their homes.

How Developers Contribute to the Bay's Problems

If you were a developer in the Chesapeake Bay area, here are some problems you might create:

- Trees help keep sediment out of the bay by holding the soil in place with their roots and by absorbing and slowing down rainfall. As a developer, you need to cut down these trees to clear the land for building.

- When you build, you replace natural surfaces (such as trees, bushes, grasses, and leaf litter) with hard surfaces (such as pavement and rooftops). Whenever it rains, these hard surfaces send runoff gushing toward the bay.

- The runoff from your construction sites is loaded with sediment. Sediment clouds the bay's waters and cuts off light from underwater grasses, clogs fish gills, and smothers bottom-dwelling animals.

- The more homes, highways, offices, and shopping centers you build, the more people move into the Chesapeake watershed area. They all produce garbage and sewage, drive trucks and cars, and use electricity. One way or another, these activities produce pollution, which travels down to the bay.

How Developers Can Help the Bay

As a developer in the bay area, here are some things you can do to help the bay:

- Try to cut down fewer trees. To help replace the forests lost to construction, plant new trees.

- While construction is going on, build barriers, such as silt fences, to hold back runoff. These barriers hold back soil but allow water to go through. This keeps more sediment from washing into the bay and keeps soil from being stripped from the land.

- Try to put up more energy-efficient, less polluting buildings, even though these may be more expensive to build.

- Plan new developments so that buildings are close together, not spread out over a big area. That way people can use carpools or public transportation.

- Build developments that protect wildlife by leaving as many natural forest and stream areas as possible.

- Try to use less pavement or pavements that let water seep through.

Trade-offs: Advantages for the Bay and Disadvantages for the Group

Sometimes what is good for the environment is hard on people. Reread each suggestion about how land developers could help the bay, and then ask yourself these questions:

- How would this solution help improve the bay?

- What are the trade-offs involved in this solution?

Point of View Sheet: Recreational Boaters

Your group will represent the point of view of the recreational boaters. These people enjoy spending their free time motoring or sailing on the waters of the Chesapeake Bay.

After you have read the selection, discuss these questions with the rest of your group as if you were a recreational boater:

- In your own words, how do you think you, as a recreational boater, contribute to the problems in the Chesapeake Bay?

- How could you help solve the bay's problems?

- Which solutions would you find difficult to live with?

- What benefits would you get from a healthier bay?

What Some Boaters Have to Say

Here are three quotes from recreational boaters in the bay area:

People always think boaters are the bad guys. When industries and cities clean up their mess, then I will be more than willing to do my share.

The problems are complex and everyone's responsibility. I'm willing to use a holding tank [for sewage] provided I can have it pumped when I need to. And that it doesn't cost too much.

In marinas, it's not so hot, with styrofoam, paper cups, and fish heads and guts floating around.

From the Recreational Boaters' Point of View

Recreational boaters have found the Chesapeake Bay to be a delightful "playground." Tens of thousands of them spend their free time sailing, motoring, sunning, swimming, fishing, and crabbing there. Because they love being on the water, boaters have become concerned about the state of the bay.

Over the past several years, boaters have complained that the water is getting dirtier. Because of algae blooms and sedimentation, the water is not as clear as it used to be. And it is also littered with floating trash: paper, styrofoam containers, bottles, food scraps, fishing lines, oil, and even sewage. The water is not nearly as much fun to be on—or in—as it used to be.

Boaters have chosen to spend their recreational dollars in this area. And they contribute a great deal of money to the local economy. They spend money to buy and outfit their boats. Then they spend still more money on fuel, upkeep and repairs, storage, docking in a marina, and high sewage pump-out fees.

Plus, boaters are having a harder time finding space to keep their boats when they're not on the water. More and more, marinas are being crowded out by other kinds of commercial development.

Many recreational boaters also feel that they are only a small part of the pollution problem. But they want to continue to enjoy the bay. So they also want to use it in a responsible way. Many support taking strong action to improve the water quality in the Chesapeake Bay.

How Recreational Boaters Contribute to the Bay's Problems

If you were a recreational boater in the bay area, here are some problems you might create:

- Although the federal government has laws against it, some of you still use the bay as a dump. You toss trash, garbage, and sewage overboard.

- Boats can spill toxic materials such as motor oil, gasoline, and antifreeze into the water. And over a long period of time, bottom paint from your boats can also be toxic to marine organisms.

- Boat marinas destroy shoreline habitats and draw additional people to the area.

- Boats traveling at high speeds make wakes (waves close to the shore) that cause shoreline erosion.

How Recreational Boaters Can Help the Bay

As a recreational boater in the bay area, here are some things you can do to help the bay:

- Dispose of trash and toxic products properly: on land.

- Install and use a Coast Guard-approved toilet on board your boat. Have the toilet tank emptied at an approved pump-out station.

- If boaters must use toxic paint, make sure to use and dispose of it in a way that does not harm the environment.

- Strictly obey a "no-wake" speed limit near shoreline areas.

Trade-offs: Advantages for the Bay and Disadvantages for the Group

Sometimes what is good for the environment is hard on people. Reread each suggestion about how the recreational boaters could help the bay, and then ask yourself these questions:

- How would this solution help improve the bay?

- What are the trade-offs involved in this solution?

Point of View Sheet: Watermen

Your group will represent the point of view of the watermen. These people make their living by harvesting seafood directly from the Chesapeake Bay. We depend on the watermen to provide us with a wide variety of seafood to eat.

Watermen set traps for crabs, dig for clams and oysters, and put out nets for fish. Most watermen use a lot of different kinds of equipment. Their work is seasonal (different kinds of seafood are caught at different times of year). So they switch from one catch to another to keep working all year long.

After you have read the selection, discuss these questions with the rest of your group as if you were a waterman in the bay area:

- In your own words, how do you think you, as a waterman, contribute to the problems in the Chesapeake Bay?

- How could you help solve the bay's problems?

- Which solutions would you find difficult to live with?

- What benefits would you get from a healthier bay?

From the Watermen's Point of View

Here are two quotes from watermen in the bay area:

The major problem for the bay is population, too many people. They built dams, which kept the fish from breeding. They dump billions of gallons from city sewage treatment plants into the bay and cause algae blooms. Runoff from blacktop and rooftops washes impurities into the bay every time it rains. And the watermen have to pay the price for the "people problem." We are the ones who get regulated.

—A representative of the Maryland Watermen's Association

Needless to say, the money's not in this that's in other jobs. But there's a certain peace of mind to it. You've got to resign yourself you're never going to be rich, just about make a living, that's all. But there are no deadlines. Nobody telling you what to do.

—A longtime waterman

The life of a Chesapeake Bay waterman is not easy—up before dawn, out on the water in all weather, muscles straining. And there is not much reward for the hours of back-breaking labor. Catches are low because of both pollution and the laws restricting how much watermen can catch. Because of disease and pollution, oysters are very scarce. Only the blue crab is still plentiful. But no one can predict how long this will be true.

Most watermen would agree that it is getting harder and harder to make a decent living from the Chesapeake. The bay itself is yielding less. And the watermen find themselves competing with sports fishermen and recreational shellfishers for the limited catch.

The total number of watermen working the bay stays about the same from year to year. But the number of sports fishermen is growing rapidly. The two competing groups have very different points of view.

Watermen go out on the bay to earn a living. So they are vitally concerned with the health, size, and number of creatures in the bay. They must pay a license fee and all the expenses (such as fuel, boat maintenance, salaries for the crew, marina tie-up costs). What's left over from the sale of their catch is their profit, what they live on.

Watermen also must obey laws about how much they can harvest from the bay each day. Before they can sell their rockfish catch, they must first stop at a checking station. There, marine police approve the amount of fish pulled in that day.

Sports fishermen, on the other hand, go out on the bay for fun. And although many care about the environment, they do not depend on the Chesapeake to make their living. Sports fishermen don't share the same expenses that the watermen bear. And they don't have to check in their catch at a marine police station.

Some watermen also feel that they are being crowded out by new development. New houses dot the area, new condominiums rise up, and new marinas appear on the shoreline. All of this can only mean more people, more boats, and more competition.

How Watermen Contribute to the Bay's Problems

If you were a waterman in the bay area, here are some problems you might create:

- Some experts think that in spite of regulations, you still take too much out of the bay each year. The fish and shellfish are not able to reproduce and replace themselves as fast as you pull them out.

- Like anyone else who lives in the Chesapeake Bay area, you and your family produce garbage and sewage, drive cars, trucks, and boats, and use electricity. One way or another, these activities produce pollution, which travels into the bay.

How Watermen Can Help the Bay

As a waterman in the bay area, here are some things you can do to help the bay:

- Some experts suggest that the best way to bring back the oysters, clams, crabs, and fish is just to "let them rest," or stop catching them for a while until their populations can rebuild. This strategy has already worked with the rockfish. But it is very hard on you, since your living depends on your catches.

- Others suggest that whenever a species becomes scarce in the bay, you should have to limit your catch on that species.

- Work cooperatively with marine biologists to set limits on the harvest. Biologists could study life in the bay and recommend how much of each species would be safe to harvest. You could provide the commonsense observations and understanding of the bay passed down through the generations.

- Support elected officials who will work for the bay's protection.

- States could enforce a two-year waiting period on licenses for people who want to become watermen. This would help limit the number of new watermen like you working the bay.

- Be sure to obey federal regulations against dumping sewage and garbage from boats.

Trade-offs: Advantages for the Bay and Disadvantages for the Group

Sometimes what is good for the environment is hard on people. Reread each suggestion about how the watermen could help the bay, and then ask yourself these questions:

- How would this solution help improve the bay?

- What are the trade-offs involved in this solution?

Point of View: Dairy Farmers

Your group will represent the point of view of the dairy farmers who live in the Chesapeake Bay's watershed.

We depend on dairy farms to raise cows for the milk and milk products (such as cheese and ice cream) that we enjoy. Often, dairy farmers raise other animals and crops on their farms as well. But cows are their main source of income.

After you have read this selection, discuss these questions with your group as if you were a dairy farmer:

- In your own words, how do you think that you, as a dairy farmer, contribute to the problems in the Chesapeake Bay?

- How could you help solve the bay's problem?

- Which solutions would you find it difficult to live with?

- What benefits would you get from a healthier bay?

From the Dairy Farmer's Point of View

Here are two quotes from dairy farmers in the bay area:

I never gave much thought to how my cows might be affecting the Chesapeake Bay. Then last weekend I went to visit some friends who had a cottage back on a stream there. I saw the water, and holy smoke! It looked pretty stale. I wouldn't want to swim in it. Or eat anything that came out of it.

Sure, I know about the Chesapeake Bay's cleanup program. A lot of the things they recommend I should have been doing for years. I'd see my cows in the hot summer when I was out baling hay, down there in Sinking Creek, and I'd know they were using that water as their own personal toilet. . . . You just put things off, and never get around to them.

Being a dairy farmer is a tougher job than you might think: getting up while it's still dark to feed the cows, milking them (usually two times a day), and raising hundreds of acres of corn and alfalfa to feed them. Plus farmers need to tend to sick cows, fix complicated machinery, manage workers, and find customers for the milk.

Not only that, but milk prices are down, and the costs for operating a dairy farm are up. One automatic milking machine costs about $3,000. And a good-sized dairy farm may need a dozen of these machines.

So for the dairy farmers in the bay's watershed—some of whom live so far from the bay they've never even seen it—the fact that their cows pollute may not be their first concern. Making a living is.

Still, the dairy farmers must do something with all the manure their cows produce (each cow produces about 100 pounds of manure a day). Most farmers use this manure as fertilizer, but there's so much of it (and more coming every day) that they sometimes need expensive equipment to help solve the problem.

For instance, one farmer said he uses a bulldozer to push the manure from the cow stalls onto a conveyor belt, which deposits it temporarily behind the barn in a huge storage tank that holds 1.5 million gallons of waste. The tank has to be emptied several times a year. And there are pumps to get the manure into the trucks, which then spread it on the field as fertilizer. This equipment costs the farmer $75,000.

Even if farmers use the manure as fertilizer, sometimes there's still too much of it. Some farmers have so many cows that there is far more manure than there is cropland on which to spread it.

How Dairy Farmers Contribute to the Bay's Problems

If you were a dairy farmer in the bay area, here are some problems you might create:

- Cow manure runs off into streams, creeks, and rivers, all of which eventually drain into the Chesapeake Bay. The manure, a rich fertilizer, causes algae blooms. Algae block off sunlight, and underwater grasses die.

- Like many dairy farmers, you grow crops to produce feed for your cows. You might use chemical fertilizers that also wind up in the bay.

- You allow your cows to wander in and around streams. When cows walk on the banks of streams, they loosen and break down the soil. It washes more easily into the streams (and eventually into the bay) as sediment.

- Like anyone else who lives in the Chesapeake Bay's watershed, you and your family produce garbage and sewage, drive cars and trucks, and use electricity. One way or another, these activities produce pollution, which travels down to the bay.

How the Dairy Farmers Can Help the Bay

As a dairy farmer, here are some things you can do to help the bay:

- Instead of using chemical fertilizers, use natural fertilizer (cow manure) to fertilize your land.

- Build fences to keep your cows from wandering near the water.

- Build concrete or steel pits for holding the manure. Instead of having to spread manure every day, you can do it when you choose (not during rainy times, for example, when runoff increases).

- Before you decide to buy more cows to produce more milk, first make sure you have enough land on which to spread the extra manure.

- In winter, when the fields normally would be bare, you can plant cover crops such as winter wheat or rye. Cover crops absorb extra nutrients that would otherwise run off. And they help prevent erosion by holding soil in place over winter.

- Sometimes when cows stay on one pasture too long, it can become bare and muddy. You can move cows from one pasture to another so that the pasture stays healthy and the soil does not erode.

- When you harvest your crops, leave some of the plant stems and leaves on top of the ground. These help cushion rainfall as it hits the ground and prevent runoff.

Trade-offs: Advantages for the Bay and Disadvantages for the Group

Sometimes what is good for the environment is hard on people. Reread each suggestion about how the dairy farmers could help the bay, and then ask yourself two questions:

- How would this solution help improve the bay?

- What are the trade-offs involved in this solution?

Record Sheet 15-A   **Team Members**   Name: _____

Name: _____

Name: _____

Name: _____

Date: _____

Problem-Solving Sheet

1. Our group represents the _____ point of view.

2. Here are some ways that _____ contribute to the problems in the
    (name of group)
    Chesapeake Bay.

    _____

    _____

    _____

    _____

    _____

    _____

3. Here are at least three ways that _____ can help solve the bay's problems.
    (name of group)

    A. _____

    _____

    _____

    _____

    B. _____

    _____

    _____

    _____

Record Sheet 15-A   Name of Group: _____

Problem-Solving Sheet *(continued)*

C. _____

_____

_____

_____

4. Solutions that have advantages for the bay but may also have disadvantages for our group include the following:

Solution A: _____

Advantages for the bay   Disadvantages for the group

_____   _____

_____   _____

_____   _____

_____   _____

Trade-offs

_____

_____

_____

_____

Record Sheet 15-A   Name of Group: _____

Problem-Solving Sheet *(continued)*

Solution B: _____

Advantages for the bay   Disadvantages for the group

_____   _____

_____   _____

_____   _____

_____   _____

Trade-offs

_____

_____

_____

_____

Solution C: _____

Advantages for the bay   Disadvantages for the group

_____   _____

_____   _____

_____   _____

_____   _____

Trade-offs

_____

_____

_____

_____

Holding the Mini-Conference:
A Look at Trade-offs

Overview and Objectives

In the past two lessons, students linked the problems from their pollution experiments with the real-world problems of the Chesapeake Bay. Students now apply this knowledge, recognizing that environmental problems are complex, involve many different interest groups, and often require these groups to make trade-offs in order to reach workable solutions. Their presentations, discussions, and questions also provide important information that you can use to assess their understanding of environmental problems in our world.

- Students present an environmental problem from a particular point of view and propose solutions.

- Students evaluate other groups' points of view and solutions.

- Students examine their own lives and how they can help find solutions to some of the world's environmental problems.

Background

As students listen to each group's presentation, they will take in widely differing viewpoints as well as numerous—and sometimes conflicting—suggestions for how to solve the bay's problems. Students may feel confused and perhaps even overwhelmed by the immensity of the bay's environmental problems. Assure them that they are in good company; when environmental problems are involved, there are no easy answers. At the same time, it is important to end the unit on a positive note and to leave students feeling that there are practical steps we can all take to combat pollution and improve our environment.

The point of today's presentations is not to solve the problems of the Chesapeake Bay but to communicate the complexities of its problems. Indeed, it would be artificial to come to closure, to decide on exactly how to "fix" the problems.

It is important to make the point that environmental problems are extremely complex and that every solution comes with a price tag of some kind, or the giving up of one thing in order to gain another. For this age group, simply recognizing the trade-offs in a situation this complex is challenging enough. Also keep in mind that a second goal of this lesson is to expand students' awareness from the pollution in the Chesapeake Bay to pollution problems that may exist in their own areas.

Materials

For each team

Chalkboard or other space to hang newsprint from Lesson 15

Tape or tacks to hang the newsprint sheets

Costumes and props to enhance the presentations

Preparation

1. Arrange the room to accommodate the presenters.

2. Borrow furniture if necessary. If you have invited guests, prepare seating.

3. Obtain any audiovisual equipment students plan to use.

Procedure

1. Before inviting each group to make its presentation, explain that the class will now hear about the problems in the Chesapeake Bay from many different points of view. Students will also listen to what different groups judge to be the best solutions to these problems.

Figure 16-1

Making presentations

2. Have each group make its presentation. Remind students to do the following:

   ■ Tell how their group contributes to the bay's problems.

   ■ List at least three solutions to the problems caused by the group you represent.

   ■ Tell the advantages for the bay, the disadvantages for their group, and some of the trade-offs involved for each solution.

3. When all groups have finished presenting, hang their newsprint sheets side by side. Ask students to comment on the following questions:

   ■ What are the similarities in the ways that different groups contribute to the problem? What are the differences?

- What are the similarities in the solutions that different groups propose? What are the differences?

- Which solutions are mentioned more than once? Which solutions seem to oppose each other?

Final Activities

1. Have students discuss the pollution experiment and its relationship to a real-world ecosystem: the Chesapeake Bay. Ask the students to do the following:

   - List some practical steps we can all take to combat pollution and improve our environment.

   - Mention some ways we, as individuals, can help solve ecological problems and maintain healthy ecosystems throughout our area.

2. Bring the project to a close with a reflective writing activity. Let students select one of the following topics:

   - Healthy plants are one key to a healthy ecosystem, both on land and in the water. Can you describe why this might be true?

   - Think about your pollutant. Describe the similarities between what happened in the polluted ecocolumn and what is happening to the bay.

   - What positive contributions can you make to ecosystems that are experiencing problems similar to those of the Chesapeake Bay?

Extension

Because some of the ecocolumns used in the experiments may have taken longer than others to show the drastic effects of pollution, allow your students to continue the pollution experiments over several months if they desire. Some students may even want to set up new experiments with additional pollutants. Remind them to make and record observations.

Management Tip

What will you do with the ecocolumns now that the unit has ended? There are several possibilities:

- Keep the viable ecocolumns in class and continue to observe them.

- Discard the contents of the polluted ecocolumns and rinse them out thoroughly (no soap). Reuse the bottles for students who wish to create additional ecocolumns using "wild" plants and animals from outside.

- See pg. 217 of Appendix A for suggestions on what to do with live materials.

Assessment

This lesson offers you several opportunities to assess students' current ability to interpret and apply information related to ecosystems. You may find it useful to refer to **Record Sheet 15-A** as a companion to the student presentations. Take note of the following when you evaluate the presentations:

- Were students able to offer solutions to the bay's problems from their assigned points of view without offering their own personal opinions?

- Were students able to discuss the trade-offs involved in their solutions?

- Did students give reasons not listed in the readings? Did they use their own words?

Post-Unit Assessment

The post-unit assessment on pg. 193 is a matched follow-up to the pre-unit assessment in Lesson 1. By comparing students' pre- and post-unit responses, you will be able to document their growth in knowledge about ecosystems.

Additional Assessments

Additional assessments for this unit are provided on pgs. 197–204. They include a self-assessment for students and environmental problems for students to analyze.

Post-Unit Assessment

Overview

This post-unit assessment is matched to the pre-unit assessment of students' ideas about the complex relationships that exist between living and nonliving things in an ecosystem. By comparing the individual and class responses and the notebook entries from these activities with those from Lesson 1, you will be able to document and assess students' learning over the course of the unit. In Lesson 1, students wrote and then shared their responses to two lists—"How Living Things Depend on Each Other: What We Know Now" and "How Living Things Depend on Each Other: What We Would Like to Find Out." Students also discussed the illustration of a riverbank environment. As you revisit the lists and the riverbank environment, allow students to record their present thoughts in their notebooks. Students may realize how much they have learned about ecosystems, dependent and interdependent relationships in an ecosystem, and how human activity can affect an ecosystem positively or negatively.

Materials

For each student
   1   science notebook with notebook entries from Lesson 1

For the class
   2   sheets of newsprint
   2   class lists from Lesson 1: "How Living Things Depend On Each Other: What We Know Now" and "How Living Things Depend On Each Other: What We Would Like to Find Out"
   1   overhead transparency of **The Riverbank Environment** (blackline master on pg. 35)
   1   overhead projector
   1   marker

Preparation

1. Label one sheet of newsprint "How Living Things Depend On Each Other: What We Know Now" and one "How Living Things Depend On Each Other: Questions We Still Have." Date the sheets and post them in the classroom. You may need extra sheets of newsprint.

2. Have the class lists from Lesson 1 ready to display.

Procedure

1. Ask students to think about what they have learned in this unit. Have them write down in their notebooks what they now know about how living things depend on each other.

2. Have students share the ideas they have written in their notebooks. Record them on the new sheet of newsprint labeled "How Living Things Depend On Each Other: What We Know Now."

3. Display the original "How Living Things Depend On Each Other: What We Know Now" list from Lesson 1. Ask students to identify statements on the lists that they now know to be true. What experiences did they have during the unit that confirmed these statements? Then ask students to identify statements that they would like to correct, improve, or delete. Again, have them support their conclusions with evidence or experiences from the unit.

4. Display the "How Living Things Depend On Each Other: What We Would Like to Find Out" list from Lesson 1. Have students identify the questions they can now answer. Ask students to share any new questions they have about ecosystems. Record their questions on the new sheet of newsprint labeled "How Living Things Depend On Each Other: Questions We Still Have."

5. Ask students how they can find out the answers to the questions that have not been answered so far. Encourage them to continue looking for the answers to these questions.

6. Display the transparency of the riverbank environment. Ask students to describe the different kinds of relationships they see. The following questions may help to focus the discussion:

   ■ Identify the living things in this ecosystem. How do the plants depend on the animals? How do the animals depend on the plants? How do the animals depend on each other?

   ■ Which of these living things need others in order to survive?

   ■ Identify the nonliving things in this ecosystem. What part do they play in the lives of the living things?

   ■ What might be going on that you can't see?

7. Ask students to look at the riverbank environment again and record in their notebooks some thoughts on the following situations:

   ■ Imagine that a group of people begin to set up a city in this area. What will change? List all the changes you can think of.

   ■ What problems might occur when humans interfere with an ecosystem? What could you do to help improve the environment or clear up the problems caused by humans?

8. When you review and compare students' responses on the pre-and post-unit brainstorming lists, consider the following questions:

   ■ Are students more aware of the complexity of relationships that exists in an ecosystem?

   ■ Have students developed an understanding of the idea that plants and algae produce their own food?

   ■ Are students aware that living things depend on nonliving things for their shelter, safety, and protection from predators or natural elements?

   ■ Have students developed an understanding that not all living things are plants or animals? Do they include microorganisms such as algae and bacteria?

9. When you compare students' notebook entries from this post-unit assessment with the entries from Lesson 1, look for new ideas, refinement of ideas, and personal experiences that support students' thoughts. Also look for the following:

- Do students attempt to describe the complexity of the relationships in an ecosystem, including those that pertain to food, shelter, and safety from predators?

- Do students mention the concept that an ecosystem can exist naturally without human activity?

- Do students mention the concept that both natural occurrences and human interference can upset the balance in an ecosystem?

- Do students use terms such as "ecosystem" and "interdependence" that indicate a familiarity with the interdependent relationships that exist in an ecosystem?

Additional Assessments

Overview

This section presents two suggestions for additional assessment activities. Although it is not essential to do both these activities, it is recommended that students do Assessment 1.

- Assessment 1 is a questionnaire that students can use to evaluate themselves.

- Assessment 2 asks students to read about an environmental problem, evaluate the differing points of view, and then take a stand on the issue.

Assessment 1: Student Self-Assessment

This self-assessment, first given in Lesson 8, encourages students to examine their own progress. By doing this assessment a second time, students can compare responses and get a picture of their growth.

Teachers have found it useful to meet individually with each student to discuss the self-assessment. Such a meeting enables you to provide your feedback about a student's work and to compare it with the student's own perceptions.

Materials

For each student

   1 **Student Self-Assessment** (see pgs. 198–199)
   1 completed **Student Self-Assessment** from Lesson 8
   1 science notebook (with record sheets)

Procedure

1. Distribute a copy of the **Student Self-Assessment** to each student. Explain that, as they did earlier in the unit, they are now going to take time to think about how they have worked during the unit.

2. Allow students enough time to complete the self-assessment in class.

3. Invite students to compare this assessment with the one they completed in Lesson 8. Students can record responses in their notebooks to the following questions:

   - In which areas do you think you show the most growth?

   - How have your feelings about working together changed?

   - How have your feelings changed about the work you have done during this unit?

Ecosystems
Student Self-Assessment

Name: _____

Date: _____

1. What important things have you learned from doing the activities in the Ecosystems unit?

2. How well do you think you and your partner(s) worked together? Give some examples.

3. Write down activities in the unit that you particularly enjoyed. Explain why you liked them.

4. Were there any activities in the unit you did not understand or that confused you? Explain your answer.

5. Take a look at your record sheets and your science notebooks. Describe how well you think you recorded your observations and ideas.

Ecosystems
Student Self-Assessment

Name: _____

Date: _____

6. Think about the work you did in this unit. What do you think you did very well?

What area of your work do you think you can improve on?

7. How do you feel about science? Circle the words that apply to you.

   a. Interested

   b. Relaxed

   c. Nervous

   d. Excited

   e. Bored

   f. Confused

   g. Successful

   h. Happy

   i. Write down one word of your own _____

Assessment 2: Two Environmental Problems

On pgs. 201–203, you will find two different assessments concerning environmental problems: "Diapers: An Environmental Problem" and "An Environmental Decision: Oil Fields or a Nature Refuge?" Each follows a similar format:

- The problem begins with three questions intended to help students focus on the main issues as they read.

- A reading selection describes the problem from different points of view.

- Two questions at the end ask students to take a stand on the issue and then back up their choice with reasons.

The assessments offer you a choice of two degrees of difficulty. "An Environmental Decision: Oil Fields or a Nature Refuge?" is more challenging than "Diapers: An Environmental Problem."

You may wish to do the assessments as a class, small-group, or individual activity. Students can give their responses orally or in writing. Decide what approach is most appropriate for your class.

When you evaluate students' responses, consider these points:

- Has the student identified the complexity of the problem?

- Has the student understood that people can hold widely differing but equally valid points of view on the same problem?

- Did the student list several reasons to back up his or her stand on the issue?

Diapers: An Environmental Problem

Let's face it: baby bottoms need to be covered. But what kind of diaper is best for the environment: cloth or disposable? Different people have different points of view on the subject.

As you read the selection, think about these questions:

- Which point of view do you agree with? In other words, which kind of diaper do you think is less harmful to the environment and why?

- If you were a parent, what type of diaper would you use? If you were this parent, why might it be difficult for you to switch to disposable diapers?

- If you were a day-care worker, what type of diaper would you use? If you were this day-care worker, why would it be difficult for you to switch to cloth diapers?

From One Parent's Point of View

We use cloth diapers for our baby. She has very sensitive skin, and cloth is softer and less irritating. I can adjust the cloth diaper to fit her exactly, too. Plus, I can rinse them out and wash them at my convenience instead of storing up smelly bagloads in the apartment until trash day.

Cloth diapers are reusable. Even after the baby no longer needs them, they make great rags and polishing cloths.

Of course, cloth diapers need regular washing in hot soapy water. Heating the water means having to burn fossil fuels. So cloth diapers contribute to air pollution.

Most cloth diapers are made of cotton because it is soft and absorbent. But cotton is a crop that is hard on the land. It requires large quantities of fertilizer and heavy use of pesticides.

From One Day-Care Worker's Point of View

I change about 75 diapers a day here. The disposable diapers are faster and easier to use, more convenient to get rid of, more sanitary because you are using a fresh diaper on each child, and safer (no pins) than cloth diapers.

Each year, Americans throw away about 18 billion disposable diapers, which, along with their contents (human waste), end up in landfills. In fact, disposable diapers make up about 2 percent of the nation's garbage.

Disposable diapers are made from plastic (petroleum) and wood pulp (trees). This uses up our natural resources. But when the cotton for cloth diapers is grown, harmful pesticides are sometimes used. It takes only half as much energy to manufacture a cloth diaper and only about one-quarter as much water. But, a disposable diaper creates half as much air pollution when manufactured and about one-seventh the water pollution.

Pros and Cons

Sometimes it is hard to know exactly what is best for the environment. After you have read the selections above, make your choice. Then answer these questions:

- Which kind of diaper do you think is less harmful to the environment? Why?

- Why might a person who held a different point of view from yours find it difficult to choose as you did?

An Environmental Decision: Oil Fields or a Nature Refuge?

In the far northeastern reaches of Alaska lies the vast Arctic National Wildlife Refuge. It covers 19 million acres of rugged, beautiful land. And it is home to 180,000 caribou, 500 musk ox, and uncounted numbers of Dall sheep, birds, wolf packs, and grizzly bears. It may also hold the largest oil field in North America.

As you read the selection, think about these questions:

- If you were a member of the Gwich'in Indian Nation, how would you feel about oil drilling in the refuge? Why might you be against oil drilling?

- If you were an Inupiat Indian, how would you feel about oil drilling in the refuge? Why might you be for oil drilling?

- If you were an environmentalist, how would you feel about oil drilling in the refuge? If you were this environmentalist, why would you be against oil drilling in the refuge? What other solutions to the energy problem would you suggest?

- If you were a representative of a major oil company, how would you feel about oil drilling in the refuge? If you were this representative, why would you be for oil drilling? What other solutions and trade-offs would you offer?

The Inupiat versus the Gwich'in Point of View

Two very different groups of American Indians live in the northeastern reaches of Alaska: the Inupiat and the Gwich'in. The Inupiat are whale hunters. They do not depend on the animals in the refuge for any of their needs. The Inupiat own oil rights to the land. They already receive millions of dollars in royalties from oil drilling companies, and they would receive even more if new wells opened up. This cash has greatly improved how they live. They enjoy off-road vehicles, satellite dishes, new housing, new schools, new roads, and firefighting equipment.

The Gwich'in Indians do not own any oil rights to the land. They would make no profit from oil drilling. They depend on the caribou as their main source of food. And they fear that the roads and the drilling activities would seriously affect the caribou herd.

The Environmentalist versus the Oil Company Point of View

Should we fight wars over oil, or should we develop our own oil fields? Why should all that oil just sit there under the refuge? We are able to save money by drilling on our own land instead of buying oil from other countries. Then we can pass the savings on to the customer.

—A representative of a major oil company

Even if they did hit a huge supply under the Arctic Refuge, it still won't be enough. The U.S. will still have to import up to half of its oil. The answer is that we simply have to make more efficient use of our fuel, and cut back on the amount we use. We should not sacrifice our only Arctic sanctuary for oil.

—An environmentalist

An exploratory oil well was drilled in the refuge at a cost of $40 million. The oil company will not tell what it discovered. It may be nothing. Or it may be the biggest oil field in North America, able to deliver up to 9 billion barrels of oil.

What if this well turns out to be the enormous pool of oil that the companies hint it is? It would keep oil flowing through the Trans-Alaskan pipeline for another 10 to 20 years. Both the oil companies and the state of Alaska would make a huge profit.

Ecologists see this as a very fragile environment. They say that we cannot predict what effects humans will have on the wildlife here. The oil company wants to build 100 miles of pipeline, 120 miles of main roads, 160 miles of side roads, two airfields, and 60 drilling pads. Much of this building would be right in the area where the caribou come to feed and give birth to their calves.

The fragile land could be damaged by digging out gravel pits to build roads, by running heavy machinery over the grasslands, and by oil spills. Human activity might drive off the wolves and bears now roaming the area. This would upset the "natural balance" between these predators and their prey.

Pros and Cons

As you can see, environmental problems are often very complex, and one problem may have many different sides. In this case the U.S. Congress must decide whether to allow oil companies to drill in the Arctic National Wildlife Refuge.

What do you think?

- Do we need the oil badly enough to disturb our only Arctic preserve?
- Are there other areas in which we can drill that will have less effect on the environment?

Give as many reasons as you can to back up your argument.

Bibliography: Resources for Teachers and Students

The Bibliography is divided into the following categories:

- Resources for teachers
- Resources for students
- Children's literature
- Videocassettes

While not a complete list of the many books on environmental topics, this bibliography is a sampling of resources that complement this unit. They have been favorably reviewed, and teachers have found them useful.

If a book goes out of print or if you seek additional titles, you may wish to consult the following resources:

Appraisal: Science Books for Young People (The Children's Science Book Review Committee, Boston).

> Published quarterly, this periodical reviews new science books available for young people. Each book is reviewed by a librarian and by a scientist. The Children's Science Book Review Committee is sponsored by the Science Education Department of Boston University's School of Education and the New England Roundtable of Children's Librarians.

National Science Resources Center. *Resources for Teaching Elementary School Science.* Washington, DC: National Academy Press, 1996.

> This volume provides a wealth of information about resources for hands-on science programs. It discusses science curriculum materials, supplementary materials (science activity books, books on teaching science, reference books, and magazines), museum programs, and elementary science projects.

Science and Children (National Science Teachers Association, Washington, DC).

> Each March, this monthly periodical includes an annotated bibliography of outstanding children's science trade books primarily for pre-kindergarten through eighth-grade science teachers.

Science Books & Films (American Association for the Advancement of Science, Washington, DC).

Published nine times a year, this periodical offers critical reviews of a wide range of science materials, from books to audiovisual materials to electronic resources. The reviews are primarily written by scientists and science educators. Science Books & Films is useful for librarians, media specialists, curriculum supervisors, science teachers, and others responsible for recommending and purchasing scientific materials.

Scientific American (Scientific American, Inc., New York).

Each December, Philip and Phylis Morrison compile and review a selection of outstanding new science books for children.

Sosa, Maria, and Shirley Malcom, eds. *Science Books & Films: Best Books for Children, 1988–91*. Washington, DC: American Association for the Advancement of Science Press, 1992.

This volume, part of a continuing series, is a compilation of the most highly rated science books that have been reviewed recently in the periodical *Science Books & Films.*

Resources for Teachers

Catton, Chris, and James Gray. *The Incredible Heap.* New York: St. Martin's Press, 1984.

A lively account of the history of composting, as well as a practical guide to how to make it and how to use it. Includes chapters on wildlife in the compost heap and why homegrown vegetables really do taste better. Full color photos.

Dishon, Dee, and Pat Wilson O'Leary. *A Guidebook for Cooperative Learning: Techniques for Creating More Effective Schools.* Holmes Beach, FL: Learning Publications, 1984.

A practical guide for teachers who are embarking on the implementation of cooperative learning techniques in the classroom.

Horton, Tom, and William E. Eichbaum. *Turning the Tide: Saving the Chesapeake Bay.* Washington, D.C.: Island Press, 1991.

An in-depth exploration of the workings of the Chesapeake Bay's ecosystem, as well as a thorough assessment of what has been done and what remains to be done to preserve the bay.

Jaffe, Roberta, and Gary Appel. *The Growing Classroom: Garden-Based Science.* Menlo Park, CA: Addison-Wesley, 1990.

A source book for teachers developing a garden-based science program. The curriculum includes sections on how to set up a school garden, as well as lessons on soil, cycles, interdependence, garden ecology, climate, nutrition, and consumerism.

Johnson, David W., Roger T. Johnson, and Edythe Johnson Holubec. *Circles of Learning: Cooperation in the Classroom.* Alexandria, VA: Association for Supervision and Curriculum Development, 1984.

> Presents the case for cooperative learning in a concise and readable form. Reviews research, outlines implementation strategies, and answers many questions.

Pringle, Laurence. *Death Is Natural.* New York: Morrow Junior Books, 1977.

> A simple, straightforward discussion of death as a natural part of the life cycle. Text may be a bit difficult for students, but teachers could use it as a read-aloud book.

U.S. Environmental Protection Agency, Office of Air and Radiation. *Acid Rain Program: Environmental Benefits.* Washington, DC: EPA Office of Air and Radiation, 1992.

> A fact sheet that discusses the environmental effects of acid rain and the benefits that will accrue as a result of the Acid Rain Program, which was established in 1990 under the Clean Air Act Amendment. Other fact sheets on the Acid Rain Program are available from the EPA Public Information Center in Washington, DC.

Resources for Students

Ancona, George. *Riverkeeper.* New York: Macmillan, 1990.

> The true story of John Cronin, who, in his job as caretaker of the Hudson River, is an environmentalist, activist, speaker, fisherman, and detective.

Brooks, Felicity. *Protecting Endangered Species.* London: Usborne, 1990.

> A simple, engaging introduction to the reasons so many plants and animals are in danger and what can be done to protect them.

———. *Protecting Trees and Forests.* London: Usborne, 1991.

> Clear text and ample illustrations outline threats to forests from overcutting to acid rain, and tell what the loss of trees means to the environment and how we can help.

Cobb, Vicki. *The Trip of a Drip.* Boston: Little, Brown, 1986.

> Traces the journey of water from its source to your home and back out again.

Cole, Joanna. *The Magic School Bus at the Waterworks.* New York: Scholastic, 1986.

> Ms. Frizzle's class takes a fanciful trip to the waterworks. A delightful combination of scientific fact and imagination.

Cone, Molly. *Come Back, Salmon: How a Group of Dedicated Kids Adopted a Stream and Brought It Back to Life.* San Francisco: Sierra Club Books, 1992.

A true story of how kids can make a difference. Fifth-graders at an elementary school in Everett, Washington, clean up a stream, stock it with salmon, and educate the public about water pollution. Clear description of a watershed. Excellent color photos.

Conley, Andrea. *Window on the Deep: The Adventures of Underwater Explorer Sylvia Earle.* London: Franklin Watts, 1991.

Sylvia Earle, a chief scientist for the U.S. National Oceanic and Atmospheric Administration, explains her concerns for the well-being of our waters. Beautiful color photos.

Dehr, Roma, and Ronald M. Bazar. *Good Planets Are Hard to Find!* Vancouver, Canada: Earth Beat Press, 1990.

In a dictionary format, gives detailed explanations of environmentally related vocabulary. Also suggests actions children can take to help improve the environment. Lists names of many organizations to contact for more information.

The Earth Works Group. *Fifty Simple Things Kids Can Do to Save the Earth.* Kansas City, MO: Andrews and McMeel Books, 1990.

Explains to children how everything in their environment is interrelated and how individuals can make a difference. The authors first outline the facts of the different environmental problems, and then suggest specific things children can do to work toward solutions.

———. *The Recycler's Handbook.* Berkeley, CA: Earth Works Press, 1990.

Provides a wealth of information on recycling, from how to get started on a recycling program to detailed descriptions of the materials that can be recycled. Includes names and addresses of organizations concerned with recycling.

Elkington, John, Julia Hailes, Douglas Hill, and Joel Makower. *Going Green: A Kid's Handbook to Saving the Planet.* New York: Puffin Books, 1990.

An ambitious guide to saving the environment, which includes explanations of ecological issues and suggests projects.

Hadingham, Evan, and Janet Hadingham. *Garbage!* New York: Simon and Schuster, 1990.

Explores the ever-increasing problem of disposing of our garbage.

Henwood, Chris. *Keeping Minibeasts: Snails and Slugs.* London: Franklin Watts, 1988.

Easy text and color photos depict the lives of terrestrial snails and slugs. Suggestions of how to collect, feed, and breed them.

Herberman, Ethan. *The City Kid's Field Guide*. New York: Simon and Schuster, 1989.

> Describes plants and animals commonly found in a variety of urban environments, including yards, vacant lots, parks, and city margins.

Homes, Anita. *Flowers for You: Blooms for Every Month*. New York: Bradbury, 1994.

> Describes 12 plants in detail and gives care instructions for each.

Hughey, Pat. *Scavengers and Decomposers: The Cleanup Crew*. New York: Atheneum, 1984.

> Describes the characteristics and habits of various insects, birds, and other animals that clean up waste materials in the environment.

Johnston, Tom. *Water, Water!* Milwaukee: Gareth Stevens, 1988.

> Through a series of activities, experiments and demonstrations, covers many different water topics, such as the water cycle, pollution, municipal water systems, and waves.

Kilpatrick, Cathy. *Usborne First Nature: Creepy Crawlies*. London: Usborne, 1982.

> Examines the lives, methods of locomotion, feeding habits, and camouflage of insects and other small animals, including snails, grasshoppers, isopods, millipedes, spiders, and worms.

Landau, Elaine. *Tropical Rain Forests Around the World*. New York: Franklin Watts, 1990.

> Describes the environmental factors that make up a rain forest, the plants and animals who make their home there, and the dangers of cutting forests down.

Ling, Mary. *Amazing Fish*. New York: Knopf, 1991.

> Explains what makes a fish a fish. Introduces some of the more memorable members of the fish world.

McVey, Vicki. *The Sierra Club Kid's Guide to Planet Care and Repair*. San Francisco: Sierra Club Books, 1994.

> Explores what people have done to disturb the delicate balance of living things and how to repair the damage.

Spurgeon, Richard. *Usborne Science and Experiments: Ecology*. London: Usborne, 1988.

> In clear and lively text, describes many of the world's most important environmental problems. Includes ideas for solutions to our problems, as well as practical activities to improve the environment. Packed with information and colorful illustrations.

Stille, Darlene R. *Water Pollution.* Chicago: Children's Press, 1990.

> A basic explanation of the importance of water and the different ways that it becomes polluted, both through natural causes and human-made ones. Easy text and color photos.

———. *Oil Spills.* Chicago: Children's Press, 1991.

> Easy text and color photos tell the story of how oil spills occur and how to prevent them, the environmental damage that results, and the cleanup operations that occur.

———. *Ozone Hole.* Chicago: Children's Press, 1991.

> Explains how ozone in the atmosphere protects the earth and how human-made chemicals are causing holes in it. Differentiates "good" ozone from "bad" and suggests ways to curb the bad.

UNICEF. *Environmental Atlas for Children.* Chicago: Rand McNally, 1991.

> Explores the world's different ecosystems, how we are damaging them, and how we can help save them. Excellent maps and color photos.

Watts, Barrie. *Keeping Minibeasts: Grasshoppers and Crickets.* New York: Franklin Watts, 1991.

> Easy text and excellent color photos tell where to find grasshoppers and crickets, how to capture them and keep them as pets, what to feed them, and how they reproduce.

Wilcox, Charlotte. *Trash!* Minneapolis, MN: Carolrhoda Books, 1988.

> Looks at different ways we get rid of garbage: sanitary landfills, burning, and recycling.

Wyler, Rose. *Grass and Grasshoppers.* Englewood Cliffs, NJ: Julian Messner, 1990.

> A detailed study of the grass plant, how it grows, and the animals that depend on it. Includes activities such as coaxing a worm out of its hole, collecting ants, and growing seeds.

Children's Literature

Cherry, Lynne. *The Great Kapok Tree: A Tale of the Amazon Rain Forest.* San Diego: Harcourt Brace Jovanovich, 1990.

> A lushly illustrated story of a man who comes to the rain forest to chop down a tree and how he changes his mind.

Dr. Seuss. *The Lorax.* New York: Random House, 1971.

> A rhyming tale of the greedy Once-ler, who chopped down all the Truffula Trees and knitted them into Thneeds. His burgeoning business pollutes the air, the land, and the water, and all the living creatures are forced to flee.

Peet, Bill. *The Wump World.* Boston: Houghton Mifflin, 1970.

> A clever tale of how a happy, well-balanced planet becomes polluted by invaders from outer space.

Selden, George. *The Cricket in Times Square.* New York: Farrar, Straus and Giroux, 1960.

A talented cricket learns to play classical melodies with his wings and astonishes New Yorkers.

Viorst, Judith. *The Tenth Good Thing about Barney.* New York: Atheneum, 1971.

A sensitive story about Barney, the cat, and how everyone acted and felt when he died. Portrays death as a natural part of life.

Videocassettes

Living on the Edge. Written by Tom Horton. 18 min. Chesapeake Bay Foundation, 1992.

This videotape is included in the *Ecosystems* kit available from Carolina Biological Supply Company. It presents a portrait of life along the edges of the Chesapeake Bay—the marshes and shallows, wildlife, and people. The film explores the pollution of the bay and suggests some solutions.

Crane River. 60 min. National Audubon Society, 1989.

A stunning film about the plight of the sandhill cranes in Nebraska. Explains the cranes' unique habitat requirements and how these are fulfilled by the Platte River. Details the controversy over the water rights to the river.

Tips on Receiving and Maintaining Live Materials

Water

Water is the single most important ingredient in an aquarium. The kind of water you provide is crucial to the survival of the aquatic organisms. Throughout this unit, use one of the following sources of water. Make certain the water is at room temperature before you use it.

- Bottled spring water (not mineral water)
- Water from a clean natural source, such as a pond, lake, stream, or spring
- Aged tap water

To age tap water, fill a container with cold water from the tap and let it stand uncovered for 24 to 48 hours so that the chlorine gas can escape.

A note of caution: Some communities process water in a way that does not let chlorine escape. Contact your local water authority to find out. If this is the case, you need to add water conditioner (included in the kit) to your tap water. Follow the directions on the bottle and then let the water come to room temperature.

You will need to provide 1 to 1½ liters (1 to 1½ qt) of water for each 2-liter aquarium. All together, that is 33 liters (approximately 8 gal) of water for the students' ecocolumns and the seven class ecocolumns. In addition, you will need to provide water for each holding tank. The amounts for each living material are indicated below.

Algae

Materials

   3 jars of algae

      Note: No additional water is needed. Do not dilute the algae.

Procedure

Open the shipping container immediately and remove the jars of algae. Loosen the jar lids so that air can circulate. Place the jars in an area that gets plenty of bright light. Or, provide artificial illumination.

Duckweed

Materials

3 holding tanks (1-gal plastic milk jugs with tops cut off or cake pans work well)

4–5 liters of water

300 duckweed plants

Procedure

Duckweed is hardy and very easy to maintain. Open the shipping container immediately and place the duckweed in holding tanks until you are ready to distribute it to the class.

The holding tanks do not need to be deep (one or two inches is plenty), but they do need to have enough surface area so that the weed forms a single layer on the water's surface. Overcrowding will block light and may kill some of the plants.

Place the holding tanks in an area that gets plenty of bright light. Or, provide artificial illumination.

Elodea

Materials

3 holding tanks

12 liters of water

53 sprigs of elodea

Procedure

Elodea is easy to maintain. Open the shipping container immediately, remove any bands, cut the tips off of the elodea, and place the plants in holding tanks until you are ready to distribute them to the class. Place the holding tanks in an area that gets bright light. Or, provide artificial illumination.

Snails

Materials

2 or 3 holding tanks

8–10 liters of water

Food supply: aquarium plants, spinach, lettuce, or fish food

30 snails

Procedure

Open the shipping container immediately to check on the snails' condition. It is important to see to their needs immediately; during shipping, snails may have contaminated their environment close to the limits of their endurance.

Rinse off the snails in one of the gallons of room temperature water you have ready for this purpose. Place the live snails in holding containers until you are ready to distribute them to the class. Remove any dead snails. It is hard to tell if a snail is dead or alive. You might have students devise a scheme, such as placing them all in one corner and waiting to see which ones move away.

The holding tanks should be filled with room-temperature water. Provide an ample supply of food, such as several leaves of lettuce or spinach, three or four sprigs of elodea, or two pinches of fish food. This will probably be enough food for a week or so, but you will know better by direct observation.

If you must hold the snails for more than a week before distributing them to the class, you will need to do the following at the end of the week:

- Pour off most of the dirty water and replace it with an equal amount of room-temperature water.
- Replenish the food supply.
- Remove any dead snails.

Mosquito Fish
(Gambusia affinis)

Materials

3 or 4	holding tanks
2	sprigs of elodea for each holding tank
	pH paper
30	mosquito fish
10–12	liters of water

Procedure

Mosquito fish do best at 24°C (75°F), but can withstand a wide range of temperatures (4°C to 38°C, or 40°F to 100°F) as long as they are not subjected to any abrupt changes. To equalize temperatures, open the bag of fish and float it in either the holding tank or other water of the same temperature.

After 20–30 minutes, remove about one-fourth of the water from the shipping bag and replace it with water like that in the tank. Repeat this process after 15 minutes. This procedure enables the fish to adjust to the new pH. After another 15 minutes, the fish are ready to be transferred carefully with the dip net into the holding tanks. Discard the water the fish were shipped in since it may be contaminated by their waste.

Crickets

Materials

3–4	holding tanks with lids
	1-in layer of soil in bottom of holding tank
1	empty egg carton, crumpled paper, or handful of leaves and twigs for each holding tank
1	lettuce leaf, slice of potato or apple, seeds, grass, or piece of dog kibble for food in each holding tank

Procedure

Prepare the holding tanks ahead of the expected arrival date. Be sure the crickets can get a little air. As soon as possible after the crickets arrive, tip them gently from their shipping carton into the holding tanks.

Crickets need hiding places. An egg carton propped open on its side works well. Dry leaves, crumpled paper towels, or a pile of twigs also will provide enough cover.

Crickets are not fussy eaters, but, if possible, provide a variety of both wet and dry food. A small piece of fresh fruit or a vegetable will provide the moisture they need. If you must hold the crickets for more than two days, replace any moldy or dried food. Keep the holding tanks in a warm place, but not in direct sun.

If you have access to a refrigerator at school, you can place the holding tanks in it for about 20 to 30 minutes before you distribute the crickets. The lower temperature will slow their metabolism and their activity level, and children will have no difficulty picking them up.

Isopods

Materials

2 holding tanks
  1-in layer of damp soil in bottom of holding tank
  Leaf matter, a piece of bark, or a slice of potato for food in each holding tank

Procedure

Isopods are very easy to keep. After you have prepared the holding tanks, tip them in. Check them daily to make sure the surface of the soil is damp. Replace any moldy food.

Advisory on Releasing the Organisms

The National Science Resources Center advises against the release of any organism used in the Science and Technology for Children program. In some documented cases, environmental problems have resulted from the introduction of nonindigenous organisms. It is also illegal in many states to release organisms, even indigenous species, without a permit. The intention of these laws is protection of native wildlife and the environment.

The organisms used in this unit were thoroughly researched before they were selected. They are unlikely to harm local ecosystems. Nevertheless, their release might encourage your students to release other organisms that could cause harm to native wildlife and local ecosystems. If you have any questions about releasing organisms in your area, contact your state or local environmental conservation agency.

Once you complete the unit, there are several things you can do with the organisms.

- Continue to maintain them in your classroom.

- Donate them to a pet shop, zoo, botanical garden, or greenhouse.

- Donate them to another classroom or to your school's or another school's science department.

- With parental permission, let your students adopt them and take them home.

- As a last resort, biologists suggest that you place the organisms in a sealed container, freeze them, and bury them.

If you give the organisms to students or to other groups, please make them aware of this advisory.

Reading Selection: Guppies

In Lesson 4, students add mosquito fish and snails to their aquaria and then read about the animals. You can use guppies rather than mosquito fish in this unit. If you are using guppies, substitute the reading selection in this appendix for the one about mosquito fish.

Guppies: Lively Little Fish

You may have seen guppies in aquaria before. But did you know these strong, lively little fish are actually native to the tropical waters of northern South America and Trinidad?

The guppies in your aquarium will be either adult males, adult females, or immature (young) guppies. As you observe them, try to figure out which kinds you have.

Notice, too, the characteristics all guppies share:

- Their bodies are covered with protective scales that overlap like roof tiles. Use your hand lens to see them better.

- They have large round eyes, and see very well.

- They have a dark line (called the lateral line) running the length of their bodies. The lateral line is made up of sensitive nerve endings that detect pressure in the water.

- Like other fish, they breathe by pumping water through their mouth and over their gills. How many times a minute does your fish breathe?

Like a Peacock

The adult male guppy grows to a length of 3 cm (1¼ in). He is very colorful, with shiny orange, pink, black, blue, or white markings. His body is slim, and his fins are pointy. He has a large handsome tail and often fans it open for display—like a peacock—especially during the courting dance he does to attract the female.

What a Mom!

The female looks so different from the male that you might almost think they were two different species of fish. The female is much larger than the male and can grow up to 6 cm (2½ in) long. She is a drab grayish-green and may have a black spot on the tail. Her fins and tail are rounded, and so is her body.

When a female guppy is pregnant, her abdomen becomes very swollen, and a black spot, called the gravid spot, appears on each side of her body just above the rear fin. She may have only one or two young, or she may have up to 50 at one time!

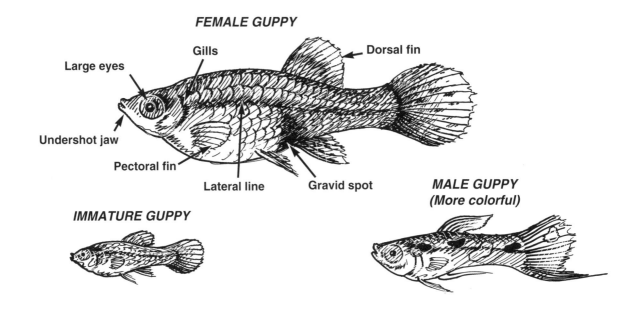

FEMALE GUPPY

Large eyes
Gills
Dorsal fin
Undershot jaw
Pectoral fin
Lateral line
Gravid spot

MALE GUPPY
(More colorful)

IMMATURE GUPPY

Babies Head for Cover

Baby guppies are born alive and fully formed. In order to survive, they swim immediately for the protective cover of plants. Less than one cm (¼ in) long at birth, guppies become adults in about eight months. Young guppies resemble females in that they are rounded and more transparent. Can you think of a reason why dull coloring is an advantage for a baby fish?

Preparing Two-Piece Bottles with Rigid Bases

There are five key steps to building an ecocolumn using bottles with rigid bases:

- Collecting three bottles for each ecocolumn
- Cleaning the bottles out
- Removing their labels and bases
- Finding boxes for marking the bottles
- Marking and cutting the bottles

Please note that the first two steps above are the same for bottles with rigid bases as they are for bottles with flanged bases (see pg. 18 for information on collecting and cleaning the bottles). If your bottles have rigid bases, use the instructions below to remove the rigid bases, mark, and cut the bottles. Information about finding and marking boxes is on pg. 18.

Removing the Labels and Bases

Have students remove the labels and bases at home (see pgs. 223–224 for instructions for preparing the bottles).

If the bases do not pull directly off the bottles, students will need to heat the glue which holds the bases in place. They can use two methods: "The Hot Water Way" or "The Hair Dryer Way." Both will work well at home, but make certain the students do not use water or air that is too hot (the water should not be over 48°C, or 120°F). If they do, the plastic bottles may become too soft and change shape permanently. Have the students follow the instructions for preparing the bottles.

Marking and Cutting the Bottles

A few items to remember:

- Decide if you would like a parent volunteer to help you mark and cut the bottles. If so, let the volunteer know the time and day your students will be performing this task.
- Set up the materials for easy distribution.
- Make certain the students do not throw away the base of bottle T. It will become the lid for the terrarium later in the unit. Students can, however, discard and recycle all unneeded bottle pieces.
- While students are marking the bottles, it is a good idea for you and/or the adult helper to circulate the room to puncture the marked bottles

with a knife. Before you make the puncture, be sure the cap is on or the bottle may collapse. Also use this time to puncture a few holes in the base of bottle T, which the students will use as the terrarium lid.

■ After marking and cutting the bottles, students will need to test the fit by actually forming the bottles into an ecocolumn. After they have adjusted or exchanged bottles to fit, have the students clean up and put the bottle pieces away. Let them decide how they will distinguish one team's set of bottles from another (for example, names or team code numbers).

Student Instructions for Preparing Bottles with Rigid Bases

In this unit you will connect three 2-liter, clear plastic soda bottles to build an **ecocolumn.** One bottle will be an aquarium, one a terrarium, and one a connecting piece. To prepare the bottles for your ecocolumn, you will need to do a few things at home.

Collecting the Bottles

■ Bring in three 2-liter, clear plastic soda bottles. **Bring in the bottle caps, too!**

■ Use bottles that have never been creased. Creases are weak spots.

■ Try to find bottles of the same brand. They will fit together much more easily.

Cleaning the Bottles

Rinse the bottles with clean water. **Do not use soap,** because it may harm the living creatures you will put in the ecocolumns later on in the unit.

Removing the Labels and Bases

The labels and bases are held on by glue. If you cannot easily peel off the labels and pull off the bases, you can remove them in two other ways: "The Hot Water Way" and "The Hair Dryer Way."

The Hot Water Way

1. Put very hot water (but not over 48˚C, or 120˚F) in the bottle until it is about a quarter full. It is important not to use water that is too hot. If you do, the plastic bottles may become too soft and change shape permanently. Use a thermometer if necessary to check the temperature of the water. Put the cap back on; otherwise, the bottle may collapse when you hold it tightly.

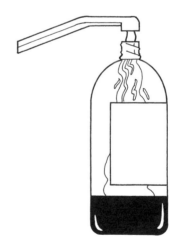

2. First work on removing the labels. Find the place on the bottle where the label is glued. Lay the bottle on its side so the water inside warms the area where the label is glued to the bottle.

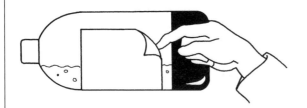

3. Wait a few minutes for the glue to soften. Then, with your fingernail, lift a corner of the label and gently peel it off the bottle. If the label doesn't peel easily, wait a little longer and/or try hotter water.

4. Now work on removing the bases from two of the three bottles. (Leave the base on the bottle that will be used for the aquarium.) Stand the bottle upright. The hot water should soften the glue holding the base to the bottom of the bottle.

5. Wait a few minutes for the glue to soften. Then gently hold the bottle and slowly twist off the base.

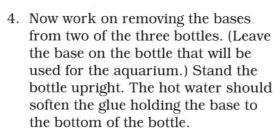

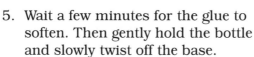

6. Remove the cap and pour out the water. Try this: swirl the bottle around as it starts to empty. The water will form a funnel shape, like a mini-tornado. This way the water empties slowly, and the bottle's sides will not collapse.

The Hair Dryer Way

1. First work on removing the labels. Find the place on the bottle where the label is glued.

2. Focus the nozzle of the hair dryer on the strip of glue for about 5 to 10 seconds. It's important to use low heat and to keep the hair dryer moving during this time so the plastic does not get too hot and change shape.

3. With your fingernail, lift a corner of the label and gently peel it off the bottle.

4. Now work on removing the bases from two of the three bottles. Focus the nozzle of the hair dryer on the bottom of the bottle where the base is attached. Do this for about 15 seconds. Be sure to keep the cap on the bottle.

5. Gently hold the bottle and slowly twist off the base.

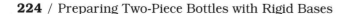

Student Instructions for Labeling, Marking, and Cutting Bottles with Rigid Bases

Materials

For every two students

- 2 rinsed 2-liter soda bottles with the labels and rigid bases removed
- 1 rinsed 2-liter soda bottle with the label removed
- 3 bottle caps
- 1 pair of scissors
- 1 marking box
- 1 permanent marking pen
- 1 medium black binder clip
- 1 metric ruler

For the class

Marking boxes

For the teacher or adult helper

- 1 knife

Labeling Each Bottle

Your **ecocolumn** will be made up of three different bottles: the **aquarium, terrarium,** and **connector.**

1. Use your marking pen to mark the bottle with the base **"A"** for **Aquarium.**

2. Turn another bottle upside down and mark it **"T"** for **Terrarium.**

3. Turn the last bottle upside down and mark it **"C"** for **Connector.**

Labeling the Marking Box

Now you must put letters on the marking box so you know where to mark each bottle.

1. Use your marking pen to write the word **"Top"** at one end of the box.

2. Measure 27 cm from the top end. Mark this point **"C/T."** (These letters stand for **C**onnector and **T**errarium.)

3. Measure 11 cm from the top end. Mark this point **"A"** (for **A**quarium).

4. Measure 8 cm from the top end. Mark this point **"C"** (for another cut on the **C**onnector).

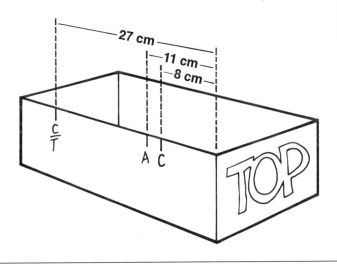

Marking the Bottles

Now you must mark the bottles with lines so you will know where to cut each bottle. Work with your partner. Take turns holding the bottle in the marking box and drawing the lines.

Note: Not all bottles are the same shape or size. When you are done marking, make sure your bottles look like the ones in the pictures. You may need to change some of your marks before you cut the bottles.

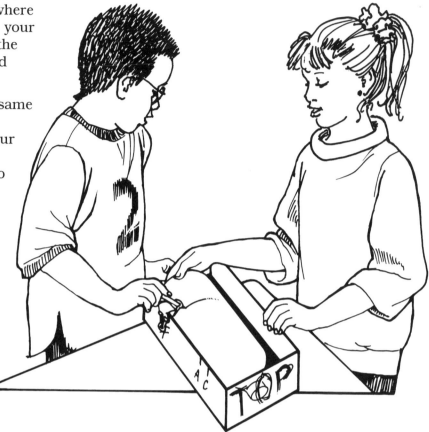

1. Make certain that the cap is off bottle **T**. Place bottle **T** in the marking box.

2. Place the center of the black binder clip down over the space marked **C/T**. The binder clip will hold your pen in place as you mark the bottles.

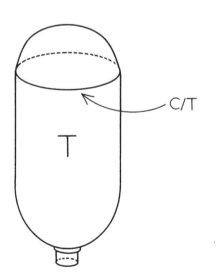

3. Push down the outside loop of the binder clip. Place the marking pen through the inside loop, which should still be up. The pen should be slightly touching the bottle.

4. Have your partner hold the bottle in place and spin it slowly while you hold the pen. Spin the bottle until a line is drawn all the way around it.

5. Take the bottle out of the box and **put the cap back on** it. While you are working on the next steps, your teacher or an adult helper will come around with a knife to make the first cut on the line for you. This will make it easier for you to get your scissors started when you cut the bottle.

6. Look at your bottle. Does your line match the one in the picture? If not, adjust your binder clip and redraw the line.

7. Now place bottle **A** in the marking box. Make certain the cap is off the bottle.

8. This time, you will put the **center** of the binder clip over the letter **A.** Repeat steps 3 to 5. Mark the bottle all the way around with your pen and replace the cap.

9. Look at your bottle. Is the line in the right place? When your line matches the one in the picture, let your teacher or the adult helper make the first cut on your bottle with a knife.

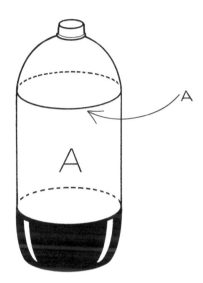

10. Place bottle **C** in the marking box. First, put the center of the binder clip over the letter **C.** Repeat steps 3 to 5.

11. Now remove the binder clip from the marking box and place the **center** of the binder clip over the letters **C/T.** Mark the bottle all the way around on this spot, too.

12. Remove bottle **C** and put the cap back. Check to make certain the lines are in the right place.

13. When your lines match the ones in the picture, have your teacher or an adult helper make the first cut on both lines.

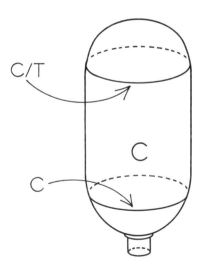

Cutting and Assembling the Bottles

1. For each of your three bottles, place your scissors in the first cut that your teacher made with the knife. Follow the line to cut completely around the bottle.

2. Ask your teacher or an adult helper to help you cut holes in the base that you removed from bottle **T.** It will become the lid for your terrarium.

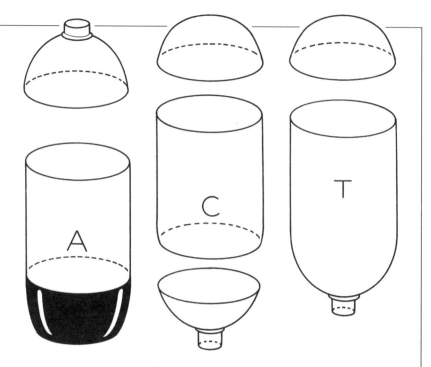

3. Assemble the bottles as shown in the illustration to the right. If the bottles don't fit well together or one bottle slides down into another, try to figure out how to adjust them so that they will fit. You may want to exchange a bottle with another team until the bottles form a good ecocolumn.

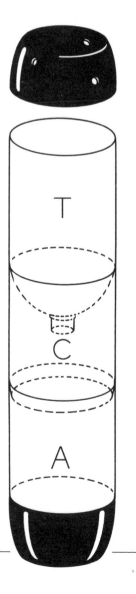